This book belongs to
Roxanne Louise Kraft

W9-AWK-008

Scandinavia

Europe

Black
Sea

Caspian
Sea

Asia

China

Pacific
Ocean

Mediterranean

India

Africa

Malaya

Indian
Ocean

Spice
Islands

Madagascar

Australia

The World in Your Garden

"Away . . . to Sweet Beds of Flow'rs!"
Climbing roses and country posies
frame the Warwickshire home
of Shakespeare's mother.

I

Kathleen Revis, National Geographic Photographer

A Volume in the
National Geographic Natural Science Library

The World

in Your Garden

by WENDELL H. CAMP
Head, Department of Botany
University of Connecticut

VICTOR R. BOSWELL
Head, Vegetable Crops Research
United States Department of Agriculture

JOHN R. MAGNESS
Head, Fruit and Nut Crops Research
United States Department of Agriculture

Foreword by MELVILLE BELL GROSVENOR
President and Editor
National Geographic Society

Paintings by Else Bostelmann

NATIONAL GEOGRAPHIC SOCIETY
Washington, D.C.

Contents

FOREWORD   THE ROMANCE OF PLANT DISCOVERY   9
by Melville Bell Grosvenor

PART 1   THE WORLD IN YOUR GARDEN   22
by Wendell H. Camp

PART 2   OUR VEGETABLE TRAVELERS   98
by Victor R. Boswell

PART 3   HOW FRUIT CAME TO AMERICA   170
by John R. Magness

INDEX   224

Copyright © 1957
National Geographic Society, Washington, D.C.
Second Printing 1959

International Copyright Secured
All Rights Reserved
Manufactured in the United States of America

LIBRARY OF CONGRESS
CATALOG NUMBER 57-11496

Award-winning roses
receive admiring glances as
Cincinnati Art Museum plays host
to a flower show.

Bates Littlehales, National Geographic Photographer

II

The Romance
of Plant Discovery

COLUMBUS SAILED WEST across uncharted seas. Braving tempest, mutiny, and the terrors of the unknown, he changed history's course, gave Western civilization a new hemisphere. But such had not been his intent. Columbus sought no new world. He sought the spices of the Indies, plant treasures of a world as old as time.

Strange, you might think, to begin the story of our gardens with spices, when perhaps we grow not a single one in them. But in a very real sense our gardens' story began that way, and that is why we tell of an age-old quest.

Since the days of Solomon, of Nebuchadnezzar, Cleopatra, and Nero, spices from the Orient had been esteemed in lands around the Mediterranean. Spices enlivened wines and preserved foods, went into perfumes, soothing ointments and medicines, and embalmed the dead. Spices were burned as incense to the gods in Greek and Roman temples; they were even believed to arouse the passions.

The Arabian Nights mentions cinnamon's use as a love philter and tells of Sindbad the Sailor voyaging from Basra to an island where he took on pepper, cloves, and cinnamon which he sold at a handsome profit in Baghdad. By the time such spices reached Europe their cost was fantastic.

Expensive? Not at all, said the wily Arab masters of this lucrative trade. Think of the perils. The cinnamon tree, they claimed, grew in the center of a mysterious lake guarded by monstrous flesh-eating birds. Only by luring these ferocious birds away with chunks of donkey meat could they rush in and tear off branches of the cinnamon tree.

To ears attuned to tales of dragons and unicorns, werewolves and witches, this sounded plausible enough. So Europe's princes paid, and learned little of their treasured spices' source. The Arabs themselves scarcely knew. They got them from India, the Indians from farther east. But they *did* know the hardships of caravan and sea routes west: camels threading Afghan passes and plodding across endless

The Romance of Plant Discovery

steppe and desert; dhows clawing along India's coast, into the Persian Gulf, or rounding Arabia to sail up the Red Sea to Egypt. Robbers, pirates, and shipwreck took their toll.

When the Crusades brought East and West face to face in the Holy Land, Europe's appetite quickened for the Orient's pungent flavorings. Today it is hard to understand this craving for spices. Pepper valued as gold and silver? Rents paid in peppercorns? Wills bequeathing pepper?

We have at our fingertips—in supermarket, food freezer, or on pantry shelf—a variety no king of old could attain. Imagine Europe's diet in medieval days: no potatoes, lima beans, tomatoes, squash, no corn on the cob. No bananas or pineapples. Little sugar for sweetening; no tea, coffee, or chocolate. With this coarse and monotonous fare spices worked miracles.

But all the spices that crowded the storehouses of the Levant were not for Europe's table alone. The spice trade was also the drug trade. Arabic medical lore brought back by Crusaders popularized the Orient's balsams and spices, believed to cure everything from toothache to raging fever.

Venice seized upon this drug and spice trade. Merchants from the Rialto met caravans from the East. Armed galleys distributed aromatic riches through the Mediterranean and beyond to Flanders; Venetian spices crossed the Alps into Germany. Crushing her rival, Genoa, wealthy Venice became the envy of all Europe. But while Europe cursed the merchants of Venice—and paid their prices—quiet events were taking place that would spell Venice's ruin and the discovery of America; that would confront Europe with Asia, and bring the world's plant treasures into our gardens.

On lonely, windswept Cape St. Vincent, where Portugal and Europe faced only a boundless sea, a man of monklike habits, of scientific bent and vision, set in motion forces that could never stop while a single land remained unknown. He never set foot on the territories whose discovery he inspired, never sailed the ships he dispatched; yet history has surnamed Prince Henry of Portugal "The Navigator."

His captains groped down the African coast, discovered Madeira, the Cape Verde Islands, settled the Azores, probed the trade winds' secrets. Penetrating ever farther into the Western Ocean, sea monsters' fearful realm, these pioneers broke the myth barrier and cleared the way for the Age of Discovery. Bartolomeu Dias soon rounded the Cape of Good Hope, laying open a sea route east to the Indies.

Then Columbus set out with astrolabe, Toscanelli's fanciful map, a copy of Marco Polo, and the Old Testament to find east by sailing west.

Everyone knows the trials of that first voyage, the Admiral's iron will, the wild joy of land first sighted. But disappointment soon tempered joy. Where were Marco Polo's "lands of spicerie," the turreted walls of Cathay? Where was the Great Khan, to whom Columbus had a letter of introduction from Ferdinand and Isabella?

Failure of a mission? Perhaps. But inscribed on history's pages are the true accomplishments of this navigator who missed his destination by half a world.

Unheralded in an age when men's thoughts burned of spices and gold were the green cargoes Columbus and his followers brought from the Americas: corn, sweet potatoes, beans, garden peppers, pineapples. Columbus saw cacao beans, which Central American Indians used for cash, and met villagers with "firebrand in the hand, and herbs to drink the smoke thereof"—tobacco.

Columbus also may have been first to observe another American gift—rubber. The Indians waterproofed clothing, footwear, water jugs with it. They made elastic balls which "being stricken upon the ground but softly [spring] incredibly into the ayer," later reported Peter Martyr.

Founding the first white settlement in the New World, Columbus planted wheat, barley, grapevines, and sugar cane. Today the West Indies supplies world markets with more cane sugar than any other area. He brought the orange, lemon, muskmelon, many vegetables, and probably alfalfa too. Today the Americas produce more citrus fruit than all the rest of the world, and the hemisphere's agriculture is reckoned in billions of dollars.

But to his contemporaries Columbus was anticlimactic. The very week before Columbus sailed from Spain on his third voyage, Vasco da Gama, in search of "Christians and spices," dropped anchor in the harbor of Calicut in India. The treasured goal had been reached . . . Africa circled . . . the spice lands achieved.

News of Da Gama's return with spices of the Indies fired Europe's imagination, and shook proud Venice to the core. And well it might, for it shattered Venice's prosperity, made a backwater of the Mediterranean. The Atlantic Age had begun, "and now it was fair Lisbon's turn."

Portuguese adventurers who swarmed aboard Lisbon's fleets made the stormy 18-month voyage to India and back with "the pumps in their hands and the Virgin Mary in their mouths." One out of three fell prey to shipwreck or scurvy's lingering death. Still they persevered and carved out a commercial empire richer than any the world had seen.

The sedate little row of spice tins on our kitchen shelf—how much adventure and history each condiment repre-

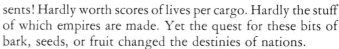

The Romance
of Plant Discovery

sents! Hardly worth scores of lives per cargo. Hardly the stuff of which empires are made. Yet the quest for these bits of bark, seeds, or fruit changed the destinies of nations.

Five ships and at least 235 men began Magellan's epic voyage around the world; one ship and 18 men completed it. Still the single cargo of spices more than repaid Spain the expedition's cost. And had not Portugal netted 6,000 percent on the spices Vasco da Gama brought back? Small wonder rival monarchs cast envious eyes.

Said Francis I of France: "I should very much like to see the clause in Adam's will that excludes me from a share of the world," and sent his privateers poaching. English and Dutch sea rovers pounced on spice and treasure galleons, stormed bastions, put populations to the sword. It was indeed a "world topsy-turvied," as Montaigne had cried, "ruined and defaced for the traffic of Pearls and Pepper."

As Portugal's Eastern empire was slashed down piece by piece, East Indiamen flying Dutch and English flags plied the monsoon seas for Asia's bounty of plants. Batavia, on Java, thronged with soldiers of fortune, buccaneers, traders from a dozen lands; "Golden Gôa" of the Portuguese went into eclipse before this new "Queen City of the East."

The Dutch kept prices high by destroying spice plants on Indonesian islands outside their control. When cinnamon prices slumped in Amsterdam, they burned the surplus. They soaked nutmegs in lime to prevent their germinating if planted by competitors. But spices were smuggled out of the Moluccas and their culture began in other lands.

Other plants drew Western ships to Asia's shores: India's cotton and China's tea. Every school child knows the role tea played in American history. Much as the colonists liked the beverage, they disliked King George's taxes more. So over the side went a three-ship cargo of it into Boston Harbor, to fan the flames of revolution. Later the race to bring Canton's tea to market established the young American nation in world trade; it created the sleek-hulled clipper ship, crowning glory of the age of sail.

Another story few will forget is the mutiny on H.M.S. *Bounty*. But how many remember that Captain Bligh's mission was to bring breadfruit from Tahiti to the West Indies? What an ironic end for a plant-hunting expedition: hundreds of young trees, gathered and cared for with such pains, flung overboard by the mutineers.

But there was a sequel. Back in England after his harrowing 3,600-mile open-boat voyage to Timor, Bligh was given command of another ship and sent to complete his mission. He did, and descendants of the breadfruit Bligh landed on St. Vincent and Jamaica thrive there today.

12

"Beauty and the Breadfruit" recalls a famous South Seas adventure.
Breadfruit were the object of Bligh's voyage on the *Bounty*;
Tahiti's alluring women, a cause of its failure.

Luis Marden, National Geographic Staff

East Pakistani tea pickers at Sylhet harvest a crop that figured in the birth of the American Nation. Enforcing the East India Company's monopoly, England precipitated not one but six "tea parties" and soon lost her 13 Colonies.

Jean and Franc Shor, National Geographic Staff

V

From the days when conquering Alexander brought back curious plant specimens from the ends of his world, plants have figured in the bold deeds of men. Captain Cook's globe-circling voyages revealed hundreds of new plant species. Genus names honor the French navigator Bougainville, Lewis and Clark, and other trail blazers who contributed to botanical knowledge. Capt. John Frémont enriched our gardens with gaillardias, phloxes, lupines, gentians, asters, and other flowers he found in America's West.

Alexander von Humboldt, explorer of the Orinoco, collected some 60,000 plants during his adventurous journeys in the Americas. Charles Darwin based his theory of "natural selection" on nature observations during his five-year voyage on H.M.S. *Beagle*, and David Livingstone discovered where our watermelon originated in Africa.

An Iroquois legend tells of a boy who braved the perils of a deep chasm, of wild animals, a serpent, and a woman who could kill with a single glance, in his search for magic chestnuts. Emerging from the earth, he scattered his prize over the hillsides, and that, concludes the legend, is how the world got its chestnuts. Fanciful? Of course. But it does suggest the hardships the plant explorer faces.

Take Robert Fortune's 19-year search for plants in the China of 100 years ago. Disguised as a Chinese, he eluded bandits on trips to the interior. When pirates attacked his junk laden with cuttings and seedlings, Fortune, weak with fever, drove them off with a shotgun. To him our gardens owe many varieties of chrysanthemums, camellias, roses, clematises, and azaleas.

Ernest Wilson of Harvard's Arnold Arboretum later penetrated the stark China-Tibetan hinterland and was caught by a rock slide while traversing a cliff gallery high above a turbulent river. Dr. Wilson was lamed for life. But that journey brought the Regal Lily into our gardens.

Joseph Rock led a National Geographic expedition through southwest China's barren defiles and across razorbacked ranges to gather 493 kinds of rhododendron and the seeds of many trees.

Man has literally remade the green face of the earth. (Remember—all major crops and most ornamentals we grow in the United States originated outside our borders.) In ancient times and in modern, when seized with a restless urge to wander, men have taken with them seeds of their favorite plants. Sailing ship captains planted seed on shores where they put in for water, so mariners to follow could harvest familiar food. Other plants traveled as stowaways, springing up in whatever country ships' ballast was dumped.

Entire plant industries changed lands. Three hundred

13

The Romance
of Plant Discovery

years ago there was no coffee in Brazil; 200 years ago, no pineapple in Hawaii; 60 years ago there was no elasticity in the price Amazon rubber barons told the world to pay.

Coffee originated in Ethiopia, but first entered commerce from the Arabian port of Mocha and later from Java. Today it is Latin America's primary cash crop. The pineapple, from Brazil, is now practically synonymous with Hawaii. Rubber moved from one side of the globe to the other.

Far up the Amazon young plant explorer Henry Wickham gathered some 70,000 heavy, oily seeds of wild *Hevea* trees and packed them in dried banana leaves. In a race bringing to mind Jules Verne, he got his highly perishable seed out of the jungle and on board an England-bound steamer. A night train awaited the precious cargo at Liverpool. Rare orchids were thrown out to make room for the new seeds in the Royal Botanic Gardens at Kew. From seedlings germinated there in that summer of 1876 and shipped in portable greenhouses to Ceylon grew southeast Asia's great plantation rubber industry, so vital to the automobile.

The cinchona was another wild tree that, boldly transferred from South American jungles to plantations half a world away, changed history. From its bark comes the quinine that enabled man to tame the malarial Tropics.

Quinine's discoverers were the primitive Andean tribes that also gave the world cocaine. They knew that chewing coca leaves stimulated them, increased their endurance; and that drinking a brew made from the *quinquina* ("bark of barks") warded off chills and fevers. Jesuit missionaries brought Europe news of the Indians' long-held secret. The subsequent trade in "fever bark" had all but exterminated the cinchona when seeds were taken across the Pacific.

When the Japanese seized Java's plantations in World War II, they sealed off virtually the whole world's supply. The United States had to find a new source; quinine, or a substitute, was vital to our war effort in the South Pacific. As the Philippines fell, a malaria-racked American officer escaped with cinchona seeds. Propagated at a Maryland station of the U. S. Department of Agriculture, the seedlings were planted in Ecuador in their native soil. Home again, after nearly a century of exile in the Orient!

Meanwhile quinine hunters—one of our authors, Dr. Camp, among them—scaled Andean passes and hacked through jungles on the eastern slopes in the search for scattered wild cinchona trees.

The search for medicinal plants continues today. No report of tribal remedy or "wonder cure" is too fantastic for medical scientists to sift. From medicine man and witch doctor have come many a valuable drug. North American

Bougainvillea,
named for an 18th century
French navigator,
billows down
Charlotte Amalie's
floral way
in year-round riot
of red and pink,
on St. Thomas
in the Virgin Islands.

Charles Allmon,
National Geographic Staff

VI

Cherry blossoms bring Japan to America. The trees were Tokyo's gift to
Washington in 1912. Embassy girls in gay kimonos light the old temple lantern
to open the Cherry Blossom Festival. Jefferson Memorial gleams across the Tidal Basin.

Volkmar Wentzel, National Geographic Photographer

A rhododendron tree, growing wild
at 12,000 feet, spreads red blossoms
against a background of eternal white.
Here along India's frontier with Tibet
rise earth's mightiest peaks, the Himalayas,
whose name means "abode of snow."
From the wilds of southwest China,
east of this lofty barrier,
National Geographic explorer Joseph Rock
brought to America 493 kinds of rhododendron.

A Japanese girl proudly exhibits
a home-grown azalea in Tokyo.
She lavishes the same affection on her plant
an American youngster would on his pet.
For centuries the Japanese have fostered
the art of dwarfing bushes and trees.
The smallish ornamentals are trained into
shapes and proportions of aged big trees,
so that a vast landscape can be suggested
within the confines of a tiny room.

VIII

Indian shamans used wild parsnip in their cures; it now yields a drug active against pneumonia and meningitis.

The *Rauwolfia* plant, considered beneficial for centuries in India, recently has been found helpful for high blood pressure and heart ailments, and as a tranquilizer in the treatment of mental ills. Curare, the arrow poison of South American jungle tribes, provides a valuable muscle-relaxing drug. Ephedrine, which clears stuffed noses, comes from the *ma huang* plant, used by the Chinese 5,000 years ago. The quest for plant sources of cortisone, in the medical fight against arthritis, has led scientists to West Africa's *Strophanthus* vine, long used to poison arrow tips; to *Dioscorea*, a yam from the Tropics; and to other plants in other lands.

"Working with plants is not really work at all," my uncle David Fairchild, the noted plant explorer, told me many times. "Wandering from village to village, seeking some new plant variety which might be worthy of sending home for our farmers or gardeners to grow—that is the life."

We would stroll among the many beautiful trees and plants in the garden of his Florida home: his beloved East Indian mangoes with their tempting, aromatic fruit; the avocados, papayas, the many palms, shrubs, and exotic flowers that he had brought back from the world's far corners.

Stopping to gaze upon a plant stranger he had made feel at home in America, he would say: "It is a great satisfaction to those who look ahead to a better world to have a tangible share in its enrichment. Without plants we cannot build the beautiful world of our dreams."

For more than half a century David Fairchild worked with plants to make a more bountiful America, and a world richer to man. In 1897 he organized the U.S. Department of Agriculture's Section of Seed and Plant Introduction; he served as "Explorer in Charge" for 27 years.

"This is the Government enterprise of Plant Introduction," he wrote in the *National Geographic Magazine* "—to introduce and establish in America as many of the valuable crops of the world as can be grown here; to educate the farmer in their culture and the public in their use; to increase by this . . . the agricultural wealth of the country."

Plants had been brought here in centuries past by missionaries, settlers, slavers, even diplomats and Presidents (Franklin, Washington, and Jefferson sought new crops for America's farms). Before the Department of Agriculture existed, consuls abroad were instructed to send useful species home. But with Dr. Fairchild's organization came America's first systematic effort to introduce and distribute new crop plants and keep close records on their progress.

The Romance of Plant Discovery

Staffed by such able and dedicated men as W. T. Swingle, O. F. Cook, P. H. Dorsett, and Frank N. Meyer, who met tragic death on the Yangtze, Dr. Fairchild's section introduced profitable new plant industries and improved existing ones. Dates, olives, avocados, mangoes, grain sorghums, cotton, forage crops, and tung oil are among them. One crop—the soybean—is now worth more than a billion dollars a year.

Nor were the "dooryard plants" neglected; many fine ornamental trees, shrubs, and vines have helped swell today's "Inventory of Plants," begun in 1898, to more than a quarter million entries. (The United States, incidentally, sends far more plants abroad than it brings in.) Each foreign plant, before going to an experiment station, must pass through quarantine to guard against insects and diseases that might threaten our farms and gardens.

The already well-traveled plant still is a long way from the bright pages of a garden catalogue. It must first survive the greenhouse and laboratory of the scientist, who seeks to improve on nature. Key to botany's dream house, where plants are redesigned for modern needs, is a set of "laws" an Austrian monk formulated a century ago, based on his painstaking study of many generations of garden peas.

Gregor Mendel died obscure, his theories of genetic behavior forgotten. Rediscovered, they opened broad vistas to science. Garden matchmakers have wed selected parents to produce such wonder offspring as hybrid corn, which yields an extra bushel in every four; tomatoes that scoff at fusarium wilt, scourge of former types; cotton with fibers 50 to 75 percent stronger than other varieties.

Here are some of the fruits and vegetables the plant remodeler is making to order for you: stringless celery; pygmy watermelons; peaches that won't turn brown after slicing; thumb-sized blueberries; redder, more attractive beets; rounder cabbages. The term "string bean" is now almost obsolete—the offending fiber has been bred out of most varieties we grow. Someday you may be able to mince an onion that won't make you weep.

The plant breeder is now truly an inventor. He can patent certain discoveries like the seedless lemon and the thornless blackberry, or floral creations such as the Peace rose. Breeders developed some of these prize specimens by years of painstaking crosses and selection; others occurred as mutations through the long odds of nature.

Scientists exploring still another avenue seek to hasten mutations by radiation, thus upsetting a plant's genetic pattern. The Netherlands has used X-rays to produce new tulip strains in half the usual period. Atomic Energy Commission experiments in radiation genetics have produced

16

Tree-ripe dates give suburban Tucson a Near Eastern flavor.
California's and Arizona's flourishing date industry owes its start
mainly to palms introduced from North Africa by plant explorer W. T. Swingle.

Ray Manley, Western Ways

IX

Boxwood grows at Mount Vernon in the formal garden patterns George Washington knew. He sought plants from Europe to improve his estate. In 1794 he ordered Bligh's breadfruit tree and other "curious and valuable" plants from Jamaica, but the shipment was lost at sea.

X

Daffodils at Toddsbury flash a golden signal of spring.
Informal plantings that grace this Tidewater Virginia home of the 1650's
contrast with the geometric colonial gardens of many Old Dominion estates.

Bates Littlehales, *National Geographic Photographer*

Bird and man bring new beauty to our gardens by
cross-pollinating flowers. Arizona's blue-throated hummingbird (above)
does it by chance, picking up pollen grains while its swordlike beak
probes for nectar in yellow columbine and Mexican campion.
Man does it purposefully. Eugene S. Boerner (right),
director of research for Jackson & Perkins Company of Newark, New York,
delicately brushes selected pollen from labeled tins onto pistils of other rose varieties.
He may make thousands of such crosses to produce one hybrid rose worthy
of a name, like the magnificent coral-red Spartan (below).

Robert J. Niedrach (above); B. Anthony Stewart, National Geographic Photographer

". . . How does your garden grow?" asks a familiar nursery rhyme. Scientists at
the U. S. Agricultural Research Center at Beltsville, Maryland, seek literal answers.
By following the movement of "hot" tracers—radioactive isotopes—absorbed with fertilizers,
they analyze plant feeding and growth processes (above). Studies with a giant spectrum (below)
reveal that red light retards flowering of some plants; infrared promotes it.

John E. Fletcher and Donald McBain, National Geographic Photographers

rust-resistant oats, peanuts with a 30 percent higher yield, even a red carnation on a white-flowering plant.

But today's scientists are going far beyond gene-juggling in their investigations. One study concerns photoperiodism, the mysterious mechanism which regulates plant development according to seasonal change in the length of day and night. Researchers have described a sensitive blue pigment as the "alarm clock" which tells a plant it's time to bloom.

Much as the poultryman tricks his hens into laying overtime, experimenters make the shrub weigela grow day and night (even bud in winter) by lighting it four hours each night. In 60 days illuminated plants grew 19 inches; unlit ones, 2½ inches. Greenhouse operators delay nature's schedule, timing chrysanthemum blossoms for football crowds and poinsettias for Christmas by interrupting the plant's night with a short period of light; this creates the effect of two short nights instead of one long one.

An exciting recent area of investigation is gibberellin, a growth-regulating substance first isolated by the Japanese. A solution of as little as one or two parts per million of this remarkable chemical has been shown to increase the number of leaves on the tobacco plant, cause earlier heading in broccoli, and speed the growth of certain flowers and trees. Other studies are being conducted in hydroponics: the soilless gardening of chemically fed plants.

Scientists who explore the mysteries of soil and sun and growing plants face a sobering responsibility. Our world every hour adds some 5,000 more mouths to feed (demographers estimate today's global population of 2.7 billion may double by the year 2000).

What could be more basic to man's existence than plants? They not only feed, clothe, and shelter us, but provide the very oxygen we breathe. Without them life would cease.

Drink milk, eat beefsteak, eggs, or cheese and you are eating grass. Our cattle graze in grassy meadows; our poultry feed on grain, which is grass. The hog is so efficient a food-conversion machine that we consume most of our corn as pork and bacon. Grass becomes mutton, wool, and the coat we wear.

Cotton, linen, silk, leather, a whole range of plastics and synthetic fabrics come from plants, as do our perfumes and beverages, our stimulants and soothing balms.

The desk at which I write, the chair in which you sit, the book in your hand all come from the plant world. Turn on the radiator or switch on a light and you are likely drawing on energy stored by plants eons ago. For the fossil fuels (coal, oil, gas) that warm our homes, cook our food, and power our automobiles and industries had green origins too.

The Romance
of Plant Discovery

Man can transform corn into sugar, and thence into alcohol, explosives, synthetic rubber, or shaving lotion. But as yet he cannot create or synthesize in quantity the original starches and sugars he needs for his very existence.

What has a plant got that man hasn't? Chlorophyll, that green alchemist which transmutes earth's moisture and air's carbon dioxide into sugar and is the link between sun and life. Ever since green matter first stirred in the virgin oceans chlorophyll has been ceaselessly creating, turning light's energy into food energy and fuel energy and giving off free oxygen, the breath of life.

As age followed age in this morning of the world, plants spread invading fingers over the land. Rudimentary leaves sprouted; roots delved in the soil. When rushlike growths swathed the earth in green, animals could leave the sea.

Ferns rose to stately forests, whose carbonized remains provide our coal. Dinosaurs ranged the earth when a mighty revolution occurred in the plant kingdom: the arrival of the angiosperms. The first flowering of the world had begun.

Some 20 million years ago the grasses spread over the continental plains; they were ancestors of the forage plants and cereals so vital to man and his domestic animals.

The Ice Age came. Subtropical forests shrank before relentless glaciers, and primitive man made his appearance. Man has since spent most of his time looking for his next meal. Perhaps half a million years he hunted, and scratched, and gathered. Only in the past 10,000 years has he possessed a stable agriculture that allowed him to lift his thoughts above his stomach cravings.

Think how much ingenuity, experiment, and fatal failure must have gone into transforming deadly poisonous cassava, or manioc, into the South American jungle Indian's staff of life. What unsung Columbus of botany discovered the food potential in this unpromising root? What Edison of the rain forest invented a stone-chip grater to shred its white pulp, flexible basket and lever to squeeze out its prussic-acid juice, and griddle on which to bake it into thin, crisp cakes?

The Industrial Revolution or a dozen Waterloos could not match the prodigious change man worked in his destiny when he learned first to reap, then to cultivate wild plants. Only when he could produce food against future needs could he settle down and build his towns and cities.

Civilization moved from toddling clothes to long pants in the valleys of the Nile, Tigris and Euphrates, Indus, and Yellow Rivers, where cultivation of wheat, barley, millet, and rice began. Here man first learned to harness ox to wooden stick plow, to sickle-harvest ripe grain and thresh it under cattle's cloven hoofs. Here he learned thrift and foresight: to

Las Palmas streets blaze with color as Canary Islands residents
spread a floral carpet for the Corpus Christi procession. Millions of
fragrant petals are woven into intricate designs for the year's hour of glory.

Jean and Franc Shor, National Geographic Staff

XIV

Flowers grow among gnarled olive trees in the Garden of Gethsemane,
where Judas betrayed Jesus. Franciscans tend the traditional
site at the foot of the Mount of Olives outside Jerusalem.

David S. Boyer, National Geographic Staff

X

save seed for the next planting, or for food when the rivers' seasonal retreat left his fields scorched and cracked.

Building irrigation works required community effort and helped weld family groups into nations. Regulating and apportioning the life-giving waters to the fields taught man government. Freedom from daily need gave men leisure to speculate on laws of the universe, to devise a calendar and a system of writing, to enrich life with arts and crafts.

In the New World the ancient Mayas founded their civilization on the cultivation of corn. The Incas rose to power on the staircase farms that march with giant strides up Andean slopes; granaries along the highroads ensured their empire against famine and ruin.

Little wonder that plants became woven into the fabric of religion, mythology, and folklore in every land. From grisly sacrifice to festive Maypole dance, earth's recurring fertility has inspired mystic rites since dim antiquity. Green growing things early became charged with meaning.

Sumatran women sowing rice let dark tresses hang loose down their backs, that the stalks might grow long and luxuriant. Swiss villagers planted an apple tree with the birth of a boy; he would grow and decline with the tree, they believed.

Our own Thanksgiving holiday echoes countless festivals of harvest-time gratitude. Mistletoe, venerated by Celtic druids, retains for us a certain piquant significance.

Reflecting ancient man's belief that spirits dwelt in plants is the curious Doctrine of Signatures, formalized from folklore by the 16th century physician, Philippus Aureolus Theophrastus Bombastus Paracelsus von Hohenheim. Not only was each plant put on earth for man's sole benefit, the doctrine said; many were clearly stamped with a sign or signature indicating what ills they would cure!

Plants with heart-shaped leaves *obviously* were intended to remedy heart troubles; the quivering of the aspen leaf revealed a cure for palsy. The yellow buttercup and dandelion were specifics for jaundice. A plant part resembling a sheep had a placid effect on nervousness or hysteria!

From such thinking arose plant names like "liverwort" (*Hepatica*), for its lobed leaf resembling a liver; and "bloodroot" (*Sanguinaria*), for its reddish juice. Some names derived simply from appearances (cockscomb, snapdragon, cattail) or real or fancied characteristics. Heliotrope (from the Greek *helios*, sun, and *tropos*, turning) was applied to plants whose flowers turned to face the sun. Lupines, Romans thought, devoured the soil's fertility; hence the wolfish name.

Others were accidental. Italians once called the tomato *pomo de mori*—"Moorish apple." But some misheard it as *pomo d'amore*, and long after it was known as "love apple."

The Romance of Plant Discovery

Man's quest for order and efforts to arrange the things around him led inevitably to the naming and classifying of plants. This posed no great problem when botany was young. Theophrastus, Greek "Father of Botany," who knew only some 500 kinds, simply separated his plants into trees, shrubs, and herbs. The Roman naturalist, Pliny the Elder, early in the Christian era, pushed the number of recorded plants to about 1,000. There it remained for 15 centuries.

With the Age of Discovery, man's botanical findings began to outstrip his ability to pigeonhole them.

Matthias Lobel (whom we remember in the genus name *Lobelia*) in the late 1500's sought a solution by grouping plants according to their leaves. Jean Bauhin a half-century later arranged them into small groups, forerunners of our genera. Soon John Ray distinguished some of the larger groups now known as families.

But it remained for Swedish naturalist Carolus Linnaeus (1707–1778) and his students to crystallize the system of binomial nomenclature we use to classify plants today. From his works emerged a botanical shorthand in which each plant is given a single genus name, identical to that of its close relatives, followed by a species name to distinguish it from the others.

In simplest terms, it is like writing John Smith as Smith, John. Smith is the family name; John, the individual.

This binomial system dissolved the threat of botanical Babel. It brought order into a science which today recognizes more than 250,000 species. Think what a task England's Kew Gardens would have cataloguing its estimated 6,000,000 sheets of plant specimens if a carnation still had to be written *Dianthus floribus solitariis, squamis calycinis subovatis brevissimis, corollis crenatis!*

Let's take a modern example of the naming of a plant new to science. In 1937, a National Geographic Society expedition under G. Weidman Groff brought back from China's hinterlands the first specimens of an unclassified vinelike plant. Its fruit, known as *lo han*, had long been prized by the Chinese for its medicinal properties.

Walter T. Swingle, Department of Agriculture botanist, studied the plant's characteristics and classed it in the genus *Momordica*. And just as Linnaeus often named a species in honor of a contributor to science, Dr. Swingle named this plant for my father, Gilbert Grosvenor, who "for many years," wrote the botanist, "has encouraged liberally the geographic and botanical exploration of China."

With publication of the plant's name, picture, and description in a scientific journal, *Momordica grosvenori* was permanently recorded in botany's international language.

Call plants what you will, names cannot convey the fulfillment to be found in growing them, the joy of making two blades grow where one grew before. Even our toil is forgotten as we rest amid the gardens our labors have created.

The returning Crusader, who brought plants "from out of the land of Saracens" . . .

> . . . cometh here full oft to seek
> The pleasant leafy shade, and eke
> His followers join him in these bowers,
> Mid mirth and joy to spend long hours
> Untouched by care.

Love of gardens today forges a bond of fellowship among the millions of Americans who plant for pleasure. It shows in friendly over-the-fence chats on how to tend an ailing rose bush or mulch a strawberry bed. From this shared interest sprang our garden clubs, and from their beautifying labors, a quickened community pride.

How did this book come about? Mrs. Else Bostelmann, the artist whose brush created its scenes from many lands, planted its seed. "What remarkable things our garden plants are," she wrote us some time ago. "We seldom realize that they have traveled all over the world; have witnessed events undreamed of by us—events woven into history and romance through the ages. Fiction cannot offer such charming and surprising tales as these globe-trotters have to offer."

The idea took root and the project grew, nurtured by my father's warm interest. Fortune favored us with authors distinguished in their scientific fields and possessed of lively writing skills: plant explorer Wendell H. Camp and U. S. Department of Agriculture horticulturists Victor R. Boswell and John R. Magness. Their articles accompanying Mrs. Bostelmann's paintings in the *National Geographic Magazine* (July, 1947, August, 1949, and September, 1951) were voted highest popularity. Members' enthusiasm created a demand for this material which, newly edited and enriched by new material, forms the basis of this permanent, reference work.

Thanks are due Merle Severy, Chief of the National Geographic Book Service, who so skillfully compiled and edited this beautiful book; and to Andrew Poggenpohl, Dee James Andella, Edward J. Linehan, and others of the National Geographic staff for their contributions to a project in which each member of The Society has had his share.

With this book as an open-sesame, let us explore the hidden world of romance and adventure in our gardens.

The World in Your Garden

BY WENDELL H. CAMP

THE WAY HAD BEEN LONG and over passes more than two miles in the air. Down to the lowlands we slithered and slipped on precipitous trails to become involved in seemingly interminable miles of mud, some of it almost saddle-girth deep.

Ahead through the mists loomed the goal, the somber ridges of the Cordillera Cutucú, one of the easternmost wrinkles of the Ecuadoran Andes, which lies at the margin of the great Amazonian plain. Only one real obstacle lay ahead. The Jivaro Indians.

Just a few years before, in a single morning, one group had made "museum specimens" of more than twenty gold miners who had trespassed on their territory. Would I encounter this group? Or possibly a more friendly one?

I had supposed that these Indians no longer practiced head shrinking, but after seeing a rather fresh relic with a magnificent set of red mustaches, I seriously pondered removing my own natural facial adornment. I was in no mood to let some Jivaro try an art job on me.

I was received into the house of the chief of the region with the customary aloof courtesy. After some hours of circuitous and seemingly fruitless palaver, the old chief and I wandered out into his garden. There, as best we could in the phrases we had in common, we talked of the plants he was growing.

The head-hunting Jivaros are excellent gardeners. Among the plants in the chief's garden were four grown in parts of the United States. One was the papaya. The Jivaros do not use the ripe fruit; they cook them green.

PART 1

Another plant which anybody would recognize by its trailing vine and bright-blue flowers as a close relative of the garden morning glory, the old chief called *ingi*. Though we seldom see its flowers here in the north, we regularly raise it in our gardens under the name of sweet potato. The other two we know only as ornamentals. The Jivaros grow the canna for food and the angels trumpet as a narcotic.

Apparently I was the first plant explorer the old chief had ever seen, and when he finally understood that all I really wanted was to study the plants of his territory, he let the barriers down. Because we had talked about the plants in his garden I was able to live with that group in perfect harmony. Being gardeners, we had something in common.

Another time I walked in a garden at Skagway, Alaska. It was 10 p.m., with the sun still shining, and I was admiring Mexican dahlias, Mediterranean sweet peas, African pelargoniums, European pansies, and South American petunias. All the while the grower and I—strangers an hour before—discussed the peculiar problems he had met, and solved, in growing these foreign plants in the far north.

So widespread are the areas from which our decorative plants have come that when we walk along our garden paths it is almost like taking an extensive tour. In fact, with just a little planning, even with no more than a small back-yard plot, anyone can truly say, "The world is in my garden."

Plants were first cultivated for food. For thousands of years previously, the wild grains, fruits, bulbs, roots, and herbs had been utilized. When cultivation began—probably not less than 20,000 years ago—these were moved into the first gardens. And so, various bulbous things of the Mediterranean and western Asia regions, which man early had learned to prepare for food, took their places beside the familiar onions and garlic. We have since introduced various of their sometimes poisonous relatives solely for their beauty.

Before the advent of maize (Indian corn) into Mexico—an event of prehistoric times—the roots of the several kinds of dahlias were an important starchy food and were grown as a crop. Potatoes, now grown in Mexico as a starch source, seem to have been introduced there from South America by the Spaniards.

One of the prettiest sights I have ever seen was a little dusky-skinned Mexican girl coming out of the hills with an armload of brightly colored dahlias. In olden times she would have brought the roots instead.

Even today so magnificent a sight as the water-lily called East Indian lotus stirs the salivary glands of many Asiatics more than it does their esthetic senses. The large rhizomes, or rootstalks, with their curious air passages, as well as the nutlike seeds appear in Chinese groceries in our larger cities.

In medieval Europe a housewife out gathering a basket of violets, primroses, or similar flowers probably was not fashioning a pretty bouquet. More likely she had in mind a tasty salad, or "sallet," as she would have called it. Once the dietitians remind us that these com-

mon flowers are richer in vitamins than many of the pallid things we serve as salads, they may again become popular food.

The invention of the sickle and the plow brought great increase in the growing of the grains, agriculturally the most efficient producers of basic food materials and also the most easily stored. This led to a reduction in effort spent on cultivating bulbous food sources such as the tulip and hyacinth. Apparently the same thing happened to the dahlia in Mexico when maize was introduced from South America.

But man is a sentimental creature. How often people have brought me plants which were diseased, physiologically senescent, straggly, and asked me what to do for them. Perhaps it would be no more than a common geranium, better replaced by one of the newer, more colorful, and more floriferous kinds. But no, the owners would not discard it for a new plant, for they had been tending it for a half-dozen years or more.

And so it must have been difficult for man to discard those plants he had carefully tended for thousands of years in his vegetable gardens. Especially since they could always be used as emergency foods in case of a failure of the grain crop.

Man also is fundamentally a religious creature, much given to watching for signs and portents. He early noted that certain plants came into bloom at regular times. To primitive man this bordered on the supernatural, and so the flowering period of various choice kinds marked the periods when he worshiped particular deities. Such floral calendars are a

feature of many primitive peoples. Echoes of these age-old rites persist in our modern cherry-blossom, tulip, rose, and chrysanthemum festivals. Thus, often starting out as foods, many plants were retained because of sentiment, or because they had become associated with religious ceremonies.

Other garden flowers were first domesticated for their medicinal properties. Foxglove originally was used as a source of medicines, notably for heart ailments (as it still is), and sweet scabious as a cure for the itch. Both were in herb gardens long before they were thought of as ornamentals.

The Christmas-rose (*Helleborus niger*), now prized for its early flowers, was first grown for its roots, which contain a powerful purgative. The aconite, or monkshood, with its spikes of curious flowers, so common in our gardens, already in medieval times was a source of potent drugs and poisons.

The roots of elecampane, a species of *Inula* often seen in herbaceous borders, once were the base of a much-used tonic. Indicating how long this plant has been cultivated, the present common name, elecampane, is a corruption of its Roman name, *inula campana.*

In the southern Appalachians, where Elizabethan English words still persist, I once came to a cabin beside which was an old-fashioned herb garden. The old "yarbwoman" willingly told me the virtues of the several plants. One was the "feverfuge," guaranteed to "chase away the fevers." In Old English, it is mentioned as "feferfuge," a corruption of the Latin *febrifuga.* Today we list the plant as "feverfew," or *Chrysanthemum parthenium.*

In mentioning a species of chrysanthemum, one is reminded of another of the same genus, the common garden pyrethrum (*Chrysanthemum coccineum*). The dried flower heads of a closely related form (*Chrysanthemum cinerariaefolium*) are the source of the insecticide, pyrethrum, now commonly used in gardens.

Color and Fragrance from Many Lands Mingle in America's Gardens. Japan contributed the *kaempferi* azaleas that frame this path in Baltimore's Sherwood Gardens. Early Turkish gardeners gave us ancestors of the Darwin tulips (right foreground), via Vienna and Holland. Manicured red cedars behind at left perpetuate the topiary art ancient Rome borrowed from Egypt.

Kathleen Revis, National Geographic Photographer

The Lover Gathers the Rose

A swain pauses
in a medieval garden
to express his ardor for a maid
through a fragrant bloom.
The rose as symbol of love's yearning
was a recurring literary theme
of his age, typified in the long popular
13th century tale,
the Romance of the Rose.
Like other flowers in years gone by,
the rose was admired
not for its beauty alone;
the quaint recipes that follow,
selected, Gentle Reader, to amuse
and delight you,
attest to a more practical role
for blossom and bud.

To make Conserve of RED ROSES   Take one Pound of red Rose-Buds and Bruise them with a Wooden Pestle in a Marble Mortar, adding by Degrees, of white Loaf-Sugar powdered and sifted, three Pounds; continue beating them, till no Particles of the Roses can be seen, and till the Mass is all alike.   *Adam's Luxury, and Eve's Cookery; or,*
The Kitchen-Garden display'd. London, 1744

To fry PRIMROSE-LEAVES *in March with eggs*   Take a handful or two of Primrose leaves, mince them very small, beat them into a dozen eggs; your pan being very hot, cool it a little, and put in a piece of butter, so put in your eggs, fry them very soberly; when it is enough on that side, turn it, and lay it in again on the other side; when it is enough, scrape on Sugar, scruise on the juice of a Lemmon or two.   *The whole Body of Cookery Dissected,*
Taught, and fully manifested. London, 1673

To make sirrup of VIOLETS   Pick the flowers and weigh them, put them into a quart of water, and steep them on hot embers, until such time as the flowers are turned white, and the water blew as any Violet; then add to that quart of infusion, four pounds of refined **Sugar**, and boyl it until it comes to a sirrup, being boyled and scummed on a gentle fire, lest it turns its colour; so done, put it up, and keep it for your use.
The Art of Confectionary. London, c. 1750

To make a tarte of MARIGOLDES, PRYMROSES, *or* COUSLIPS   Take [such] floures and perboyle them tender, then strayne them with the yolckes of three or foure egges, and swete curdes, or els take three or foure apples, and perboyle wythal and strayne them with swete butter and a lyttle mace and so bake it.
A Proper Newe Booke of Cokerye [mid-
16th century]

To make Ices of VIOLETS, JESSAMINES, *and* ORANGE-FLOWERS   Pound a Handful of Violets and pour about a Pint of hot Water upon; let them infuse about an Hour; put about half a Pound of Sugar; when it is properly dissolved, sift through a Napkin. The Jessamine [and Orange-Flowers] are done after the same Manner . . .; those different

Pyrethrum, however, apparently was not first used to control garden pests. Rubbed on fresh, or preferably applied as a powder to the skin and clothes, it seems to have been used against such things as body lice and fleas. In the South American Andes I found the Quechua-speaking Cholos using other plants, not too distantly related to the pyrethrum, as a cure for "nervousness" in infants.

Anyone who has lived with these people knows that much of this infant "nervousness" is due to biting insects. I therefore suspect that man's interest in chrysanthemums as a source of insect powders may go back much farther than his appreciation of them as garden decoratives. And I suppose that even the little wild pansy, in England and sometimes

Infusions are also mixed with Cream, instead of Water. The Cream or Mixture being prepared, put it in the Icing-pot [then] in a proper Tub, and pounded Ice with Salt sufficient, to bury the Pot in it, stirring continually with a flat Pewterspoon, till it begins to freeze; work the Ice so in freezing, that it may not be in harder Flakes in one Part than another; only put them in the proper Moulds a little while before serving. *The Art of Modern Cookery Displayed . . . Translated from Les Soupers de la Cour, ou, La Cuisine Reformée . . . By a Foreigner, who has been several years a Clerk of the Kitchen in Noble Families in this Kingdom. London, 1767*

Of the FLOURE OF THE SUN, or THE MARIGOLD OF PERU We have found by triall, that the buds . . . boiled and eaten with butter, vineger, and pepper, after the manner of Artichokes, are exceeding pleasant meat, surpassing the Artichoke far in procuring bodily lust. *The Herball or General Historie of Plantes, gathered by John Gerarde, Master in Chirurgerie. London, 1633*

here called heartsease, might be classed as a medicinal plant of sorts, for in the olden days a decoction of it was administered to cure the pangs of love. Our modern English name "pansy" comes from the French word *pensée*, and, as the old poem indicates, the malady might become serious:

Why so *pensive*, little maid?
Prithee, why so pale?

And if the little lady were having the "vapors" and going into a decline over the affair, she would be given an extract of rue as a tonic. The younger generation is now more philosophical about such matters of the heart, but we still grow heartsease and rue in our gardens.

Our flowers came into gardens in yet other ways. In days when bathing was not too convenient, a lady had to disguise the fact as well as possible. She used the somewhat sweet-scented orris-root both as a perfume and as a dusting powder. The word "orris" is a corruption of *iris*, and the source of this material is the powdered root of the Florentine iris, an ancestor of the more common of our modern garden groups of this genus.

Flowers which came into gardens first as the sources of perfumes and toilet waters—again as substitutes for soap and water—would make a long list indeed. Legend tells of a certain ancient oriental potentate who ordered that his bath water always have steeped in it a mass of rose petals. However, he noted a slight oily scum on the water. Disliking this seeming contamination, he ordered it skimmed off; whereupon it was discovered that this oily substance was the real source of the rose odor.

While this story may be apocryphal, the fact remains that the toilet water used by polite ladies for their occasional sponge baths until bathtubs came into fashion was no more than an infusion of flowers in water.

But things really were not so bad as they might seem, for almost every region has some

It's *spring in Flanders and a prosperous householder directs work in the privacy of* his town garden. The time: the Renaissance; late 15th century, if you will. But chessboard pattern reminds of medieval days when each square was planted to its own herb for kitchen, for essence, or for cure.
Flowers, as well, grow here to pleasure the master's eye and bring zest to family fare. Slant-roofed wing near well at rear houses gardeners, produce, and tools.

Bettmann Archive

To make MARYGOLD *Cheese*   Gather your Marygold Flowers in a dry Day, and pick the golden-colour'd [petals] . . . bruise them in a Mortar, or grind them . . . and strain; this Juice, when you put the Rennet to the Milk, must be put into the Milk, and stirr'd into it. The Milk must then be set, and as soon as the Curd is come, break it gently, and as equally as possible, and put it into the Cheese Vat, and press it with a gentle Weight, letting the bottom part of the Vat have such a number of Holes in it, as will let out the Whey.

The Country Housewife
and Lady's Director. London, 1736

To pickle any kind of Flowers for SALLETS *&c.*   Put them into a gally-pot or double glass, with as much sugar as they weigh, fill them up with wine vinegar; to a pint of vinegar a pound of sugar, and a pound of flowers; so keep them for sallets or boild meats in a double glass covered over with a blade and leather.

The Accomplisht Cook. London, 1685

ROSE *Pie*   Take fresh roses, strip the leaves, remove the white [from the petals], put them in a mortar; pour on some broth and strain. Skin four cooked calves' brains and remove the nerves; grind eight scruples of pepper moistened with the juice and rub. Break eight eggs, add one half ladle of wine, one ladle of raisin wine and a little hot oil. Grease a pan, place it on the hot ashes and pour in the mixture; when it is cooked sprinkle with pulverized pepper and serve.

Apicius de re Coquinaria. Rome,
100 B.C. (?); perhaps the oldest cookbook extant

COWSLIP *Pudding*   Get about half a peck of cowslips, pick the flowers off, chop and pound them fine, with a quarter of a pound of Naples biscuit grated, and a pint and a half of new milk or cream, boil them altogether a little . . . beat up the yolks of eight and the whites of four eggs with a little cream and a spoonful of rose water, sweeten it to your palate, mix all well together, put it over a slow fire, keep it stirring till it is thick, and then set it away to cool; lay a puff-paste round the edge of the dish, pour in the pudding, and bake it half an hour; sprinkle some fine powdered sugar over it, and send it to table hot.

The New Art of Cookery. Philadelphia, 1792

28

plant which, when rubbed in water, makes a soapy lather. The people of Europe and Asia Minor, for example, had several species of *Saponaria*, or soapwort. After man learned to make soap from an extract of wood ashes and hot fat, some of the soapworts stayed on in flower gardens.

One came to America and is a common garden inhabitant which sometimes strays away to become a roadside weed, usually under the name of Bouncing Bet. This is the American form of the English name Bouncing Betsy. And if you are curious as to how *that* name became attached to this plant, you will have to refer to a dictionary of 17th and 18th century English slang or go down into the back coves of the southern Appalachians where it still is used. If you lack opportunity to do either, just remember that this plant was long associated with household laundering, and then imagine the rear view of a buxom and billowy laundry maid as she vigorously scrubbed her clothes.

As civilization developed, scratch crops gave way to systematic cultivation. Agricultural tools were invented, new field methods and garden procedures developed. Efficient crops displaced poorer-yielding ones. Along with his developing civilization man's esthetic sense also was awakening. Ultimately,

instead of being entirely utilitarian, many plants with showy flowers were cultivated solely for their beauty. From such evidences as we have, this beauty appreciation seems scarcely more than 10,000 years old.

Where is a plant really native? This is sometimes extremely difficult to determine. Hollyhocks often seed themselves along embankments, finally appearing to be native. The blackberry-lily has in places become a denizen of fence rows. Yet both, Chinese in origin, have escaped from gardens.

High in the South American Andes in Ecuador I once came to a moist place where I found the African calla, the southern European iris, and the northern European pansy, all three growing in profusion and apparently perfectly at home with the native plants. Fifty yards away some stones showed where a house of the early Spanish era had stood.

We may deduce that the owner had brought with him plants growing in his garden in Spain. When the jungle again took over, these three evidences remained of man's migrations and his love of familiar flowers.

The East Indian lotus has always been a problem, for it is a double-threat migrator. Man has long used its tuberous rootstocks and seed for food; the seeds are easily trans-

UPID *stands atop the fountain in this pleasure garden of 1580; raised planting beds curve round its base. The setting is France or Flanders, but the garden borrows its symmetry, and statuary, from Italy. Vine-clad gallery mimics a cloister, but often echoes to worldly revels. Gardeners graft and prune while two ladies of the house tend flowers in courtly attire.*

Bettmann Archive

ported and viable for a long time. And such is the beauty of the flowers that they early became attached to religious ceremonies.

Botanists have thus found the lotus apparently growing naturally in such far-apart areas as Egypt, China, and northern Australia. The evidence, however, points to an origin in southeastern Asia. The story of its wanderings is the story of the early migrations of peoples from southeastern Asia down through the islands of the East Indies, of their contacts with the Chinese, and of their commerce with India and ultimately with Egypt.

Further examples are the Cherokee rose and the peach. When André Michaux came to America seeking new plants for European gardens (he was first to bring the Catawba rhododendron and the flame azalea into cultivation), he found growing abundantly in what are now our southeastern States a beautiful wild rose. Later called the Cherokee rose, it has been adopted as the State flower of

Georgia. To our surprise, the Cherokee rose has since been shown to be native to China. The Cherokee rose apparently was originally taken overland from China to Persia, there to be picked up by Moslem Arabs and carried with them when they planted their gardens in Spain. The Spaniards later brought the plant to Florida, whence it escaped to become perhaps the most common and most celebrated "wild" rose in parts of the South.

Similarly, when William Penn was negotiating with the Indians for "Penn's Woods," he found the savages cultivating the peach in

The Family Gardens Together in Victoria's Day. "The most healthy employment and most delightful recreation" man can enjoy—this is English gardening in the 1860's. Yet daintily wielded rake and shouldered spade suggest more fashion than fun, and heavy toil still falls to the hired gardener tending the trellised ivy.

Gone are formal elegance and parklike landscape of the century past. Symmetrical flower beds, vestiges of the Middle Ages, await potted plants that wintered in the sun room. Old bowling green is now a shrub-flanked lawn.

Bettmann Archive

their gardens. The peach is not a native American; it is a native of China and first came to North America by the same route as did the Cherokee rose. Being a food plant, it was artificially spread on this continent with greater rapidity. The peaches which certain of our southwestern Indians raise were introduced by Padre Junípero Serra's co-workers into the Californian missions from trees grown in Mexican gardens, also introduced there by the Spaniards.

"And the Lord God planted a garden eastward in Eden . . . and . . . took the man, and put him into the garden . . . to dress it and to keep it."

As an old man sitting in the tents of his people in the land of Canaan, Abraham must have recounted the scenes of his youth in the neighborhood of Ur of the Chaldees. These stories became part of the lore of his descendants. Thus when the later Hebraic scribe set down the early history of his people, he had Adam placed in a *planted* garden full of all manner of animals. Regardless of the other implications of the story, the Garden of Eden, so described, was typical of the artificially planted, royal game preserves (called gardens) already present in the valley of the Euphrates at the time of Abraham's youth.

We know all too little of the early peoples who lived in the valleys of the Tigris and Euphrates. Yet the Sumerians and Akkadians certainly must have had gardens. And there were the Elamites, whose principal city Susa was destined under the later Persians to become a famous horticultural center and the source of many of our garden decoratives (for example, *Crocus susianus* and *Iris susiana*). It was in Susa (called Shushan in the first chapter of the Book of Esther) that King Ahasuerus held a garden party that lasted 180 days.

The writings of one Assyrian king, Sennacherib, tell us at great length of his gardens;

Wrapped Up in Herbs, She Goes Forth Safe from Cholera. Thus did an artist lampoon superstitions which spread during a 19th century epidemic in Vienna. Windmill on her hat is to chase away evil winds. Bottles of chloride of lime dangle from her umbrella, bags of aromatic herbs adorn her skirt. Earring pendants are garlic bulbs. Massive shoes prevent infection from the street. Her dog's placard reads "Nothing to fear now."

of plants they contained which were more fruitful than in their native homes, of the many expeditions he had sent to get them, of his extensive irrigation systems, and of the many garden pools he built.

His grandson Assurbanipal, who reigned in the seventh century B.C., left us a fine set of carvings on the walls of the north palace at Kuyunjik which tell us much about the Assyrian garden of his day. The reign of Assurbanipal is important in the history of gardening, for it was he who pushed the Assyrian Empire into Egypt, bringing the peoples of the Tigris and Euphrates for the first time into close contact with the Egyptians and the Egyptian garden. (Continued on page 41)

The Art of Flower Arranging

A GIRL IN A KIMONO KNEELS before an alcove in her Tokyo home, a tray of iris at her side. Wing-like sleeves sway as she trims three stalks and wedges them into a curving vase. First, the longest stalk: the "heaven" line. Then one arcing to the side; it represents man. Finally the shortest, symbolizing earth. She bows. Almond eyes sweep upward, viewing vase, water, flowers. It is good. Her display links man with heaven and earth as Confucius taught. Her ritual, steeped in 14 centuries of tradition, is *Ikebana*: the art of "making flowers live."

In Japanese legend flower arranging began when early priests rescued storm-strewn flowers and placed them before Buddha's shrines. Journeying scholar Ono-no-Imoko learned Chinese flower ritual; at a Kyoto temple he founded *Ikenobo*, Japan's original school of floral art. The art later escaped the temple, grew less formal. Emperors, feudal nobles—even warlike samurai—arranged flowers as respite from worldly stress. As aristocracy declined, commoners came to express their innate love of nature through Ikebana's rites. Women, like those shown receiving instruction below, came to predominate in what had long been a man's art.

Rare today is the Japanese without some knowledge of flower arrangement, or the home without its *tokonoma*—the flower alcove, once a family shrine. A host compliments a guest when he proffers stalks or branches and asks him to arrange them. Line dominates the arrangement, symmetry is avoided. The holly blossom signifies a snow-capped mountain; bamboo speaks strength; the dried leaf reminds of death's inevitability.

Museum of Fine Arts, Boston

Half a world away, flower art grew more slowly. Egyptians, true, placed the sacred lotus in a vase to honor the goddess Isis, and brightened the banquet table with bowls of blossoms. But Greeks and Romans more often wore their flowers as wreaths and garlands, and medieval gardeners prized them more as flavorings or "simples." Not until the 17th century did Western bouquet art come into its own.

Great explorations had introduced flowers from far-off lands; printing helped spread the gardener's lore. When art patronage shifted from Church and nobility to prosperous burgher, Flemish masters painted the sumptuous still life for him—flowers clustered in massive, symmetrical Baroque style, vibrant with color.

Western flower arrangement followed no formal school, embodied no symbolism. It mirrored instead many period modes: French Rococo, marked by airy grace; Georgian, dignified and elegant; Victorian, crowded and embroiderylike.

Noted authority Frances Luna Ash created for this book these arrangements, painted by National Geographic artist Walter A. Weber. They reflect modern American use of Europe's emphasis on mass and color, and Japan's line and restraint.

Let these nine basic designs be a springboard for your own creative expression. Devising striking individual displays, you will find new enjoyment in the world of beauty in your garden.

Heaven

Man

Earth

...each symbolic iris seeks its place in nature's realm.
A love of all creation is here expressed in classic Japanese line,
for "flower arrangements are the mirror of the soul."

Barberry bends
like the archer's bow
in graceful <u>Moribana</u> style.
Broad water span reveals the season, spring;
in winter it retreats before the moss. Thus Japanese
today portray a naturalistic landscape in shallow-sided bowl.

"The eye hath
this sort of enjoyment
in winding walks and
serpentine rivers," wrote
the master satirist Hogarth
in a more gentle mood.
His "line of beauty"
was the long S-curve,
beloved in art today
as it was two
centuries ago.
Deutzia and
azalea trace it from
an alabaster chalice.

Flowers massed in
oval form reflect the dignity
of Georgian England. Here a stately
symmetry reminds of polished rhymes of Pope;
the elegance of Chippendale;
a Reynolds portrait.

The pyramid form,
like floral candelabra, evokes
gay ghosts in peruke and brocade...the airy spirit
of Versailles salon and King Louis's court. Double stocks and
chrysanthemums soar from alabaster urn; graceful ivy trails below.

A modern form,
the L-shape...
but its angle speaks
the timeless truth
of Euclidean geometry.
It mirrors in gladioli
yet another age-old sign:
the coupling of heaven and earth;
they meet, but will never cross.

The crescent, universal symbol
for the moon, denoted passiveness
to old astrologers; it rippled on Turkish
battle banners too. Here wrought in roses it
may mean no more to modern eyes than the challenge of
an incompleted line. For simple beauty is that not enough?

Irises clustered
in vertical form
reach heavenward.
No symbolism here,
yet one inclined
might read in it
a tale of man's
ageless aspirations.

A horizontal bank of flowers suggests
repose—a single, peaceful line not
without its strength. As Keats proclaimed,
"Oh! what a power has white simplicity!"

Prior to this, gardens of the Tigris and Euphrates region had been planted in an informal, more or less haphazard manner. The Egyptian garden, however, was planted in a geometric pattern. Thus formal planting came to this old Mesopotamian garden center.

Increasing aridity in the region made irrigation more and more necessary. This brought a system of hillside terrace farming. When incorporated into ornamental and pleasure gardening, it was called the "hanging garden." In reality, these hanging gardens were series of terraces, their outer edges supported by pillars. Sometimes the pillars were of brick, and hollow so that they might be filled with earth and accommodate roots of large trees.

Occasionally these hanging gardens were wide-based towers. Nebuchadnezzar the Great seems to have built one of these for his little bride, homesick for the green hills of her native Media. Husbands still can feel kinship with old Neb when the little woman pointedly remarks that it is about time to get out into the garden and do the spring spading.

The Greek historians Strabo and Diodorus saw one of these hanging gardens before it crumbled. They tell us it was about 1,500 feet long on one side, set back in ascending terraces, and because of the plants it held it looked like a green mountain. The topmost terrace, site of the principal garden, was supported by a hollow arch 150 feet high.

In 539 B.C. the Chaldean Empire collapsed under the attack of Cyrus, the Persian. The Persians already had garden traditions, but, now in full power, they began a new cycle of intensive garden development.

The idea of the formal garden with equally spaced plants in rows had been brought into Mesopotamia in the time of Assurbanipal. Under the Persians this developed into a real system, especially with the advent of more and more purely ornamental plants and flowers. The Persians considered horticulture a royal occupation, and special instruction in the art was conducted by and for the nobility. Cyrus is reputed to have boasted that he designed his own palace gardens and even set out many of the plants himself. By 330 B.C., when Alexander the Great looked on the dead body of the last of these Persian monarchs, the Persian garden had developed into a thing of remarkable beauty.

The Greeks did not destroy the gardens they found, as some other conquerors have done. Instead, they cherished them and encouraged their cultivation. Marveling at their beauty and magnificence, the Greeks "discovered" the Persian gardens and brought back to Europe some of the plants they contained. But it was the Romans, somewhat later, who really did the job.

So far we have merely mentioned Egypt, noting that the formal garden came into Mesopotamia from there during the seventh century B.C. Let us roll back the centuries again and see what had been happening in Egypt.

When the doors of recorded history begin to swing open along the Nile, the art of gardening already had developed to a remarkable degree. Fortunately, these early Egyptians left us carvings and paintings depicting not only the general plan of their gardens but also many of the plants they contained.

From such garden pictures we may readily note that not all the plants they grew were native in the immediate region. Already many of them had been introduced. To help us in this conclusion, we have other carvings showing vessels with their decks crowded with trees and other plants being brought to Egypt. One of these carvings records a notable plant-hunting expedition sent by Queen Hatshepsut to the "Land of Punt."

The love of ornamental plants and flowers finally became so marked in Egypt that Rameses the Great is said to have boasted that he had furnished at least 19,000,000 ceremonial bouquets to the temples. Other items we take for granted in our everyday lives can be traced back to this Egyptian love of garden plants and flowers.

At some time in their past the Egyptians had begun decorating their temples with sprays of leaves and flowers. Later they decorated the supporting columns with carved flowers, favorite among them the water-lily. The palm leaf, papyrus, and other plant designs were also used. The papyrus design, for example, was made to simulate a bundle of the reedy stems capped by the spreading tops. When stylized and worked in stone, this became a fluted column. The Greeks may have

picked up this architectural item from the Egyptians. It survives to this day in the fluted columns of many of our public buildings.

Another thing the Egyptians started: they painted their walls and floors with garden scenes. The Romans took over this custom and excellent examples of their garden scenes are to be found in the excavations at Pompeii. We got the idea from the Romans, and it still survives in our modern figured wallpaper.

Early Persian travelers apparently also saw this Egyptian custom and copied it. But with the chilly Persian winters bringing cold walls and clammy tile floors, they had their garden scenes woven into warm rugs to be used both

Metropolitan Museum of Art

as wall hangings and as floor coverings. Since many basic elements of rug design go back to the Persians, our modern figured rugs thus actually trace their lineage to those paintings Egyptians made on floors and walls to bring their gardens indoors.

Some time ago I stepped inside a Fifth Avenue flower shop to examine a display of miniature gardens in glass bowls. I was curious only to see the kinds of plants they contained. When the salesgirl asked if I wished to purchase one, I astonished her by replying that I really didn't want to invest in a Garden of Eden. Why had I called it that?

About the time Hammurabi was founding the first Babylonian Empire a group of peoples migrating eastward from what is now Persia entered and conquered India. This was more than a thousand years before Assurbanipal brought back to Persia the idea of the formalized Egyptian garden. Consequently, these early emigrants took along with them the original style of the informal, parklike planted garden, often with its animals.

("But today's garden in India is rather formal," the recent visitor might comment. This is because later conquerors who overran the subcontinent from the seventh to the 13th centuries of our own era brought the Persian garden to India a second time, this time with its straight rows and formalized planting.)

Some time between 600 and 500 B.C. Siddhartha Gautama, founder of Buddhism, was born in what is now a jungle region bordering Nepal. After his revelation under the bo-tree (botanically, a species of fig called *Ficus reli-*

giosa, commonly planted along streets and in gardens in warm regions), Gautama went to Benares. There he and his first converts built shelters for themselves in the "deer park," a garden in the style of the old game preserve.

From the first, the teachings of Gautama had been carried on in the quiet of a naturalistic garden, and from this arose the tradition among his followers that their most effective work would be accomplished in the same environment. The missionaries, therefore, took with them not only the Buddhist teachings but the tradition of the informal garden.

By the latter part of the third century B.C. Buddhist missionaries were pushing across the passes into central Asia and ultimately into China. In China the Buddhist garden underwent great development through the centuries. When Marco Polo, visiting China between A.D. 1272 and 1293, saw such royal gardens as those of Kublai Khan at Xanadu and at Cambaluc, he was astonished at their magnificence.

The lesser folk of China copied these royal gardens but, lacking space, reduced them in size, employing artificially dwarfed trees to keep the over-all landscape in scale. And if one had no plot of ground, one bought a dish and in it planted an even smaller model which could be grown in a sunny window. When the Chinese garden was introduced into Japan by later Buddhist missionaries, the miniature garden went along, there to be even more ritualistically arranged.

Perhaps you own one of these overcrowded and usually poorly arranged imitation Chinese dish gardens. If so, you have the satisfaction of knowing that your little garden-in-a-fishbowl is a direct descendant—by way of the Chinese gardens Marco Polo saw and of the Indian garden where Gautama preached—of the royal game preserve and hunting park which already was common in Mesopotamia when Abraham left Ur of the

More than 3,450 Years Ago, Explorers Brought Plants to Queen Hatshepsut's Garden. Frankincense (*Boswellia*) trees, roots packed in baskets or cloth, are here carried to the Egyptian ruler's ships at Punt, believed to be on the Somali coast. The voyage took place in 1495 B.C. This cast in the Metropolitan Museum of Art reproduces carvings in Hatshepsut's temple at Thebes.

Chaldees to go over into the land of Canaan. It is, therefore, a miniature Garden of Eden.

Two acquaintances of mine, who also are neighbors, are fast friends. They agree on almost everything except their gardens.

One garden has a central stretch of lawn, with a pool shaded by a graceful birch tree at its end. Bordering the lawn is a mixture of flowering shrubs and herbaceous perennials, with here and there sprightly touches from small groups of annuals. It is a completely informal affair, yet there is no time between April and October when some floral surprise is not peeping out from an odd corner.

Across the dividing line, in the other friend's garden, one finds closely clipped hedges and planted beds in geometric form. The beds contain flowers, but only those sorts which will not interfere with the neatness of the design. Near the corners stand four yews, so carefully trimmed and trained that they scarcely are recognizable as such until closely examined. At the center of this formal garden a bird-bath stands on a pedestal.

Each of my friends has followed an ancient custom of garden making.

From carvings it seems that the Egyptians sometimes clipped and trained their shrubs and trees. Apparently the Romans picked up the idea from the Egyptians (certainly not from the Persians) and carried this topiary work to great lengths. Ultimately, clumps of trees and shrubs in the Roman garden were trimmed to resemble such things as ships in full sail, or hunting scenes complete with stag and hounds in full flight.

Then, for about a thousand years, Europe was wrapped in the "Dark Ages."

In 1471, six years after printing presses were set up in Italy, a manuscript written a century earlier by Pietro Crescenzi of Bologna was published. This *Opus Ruralium Commodorum* had been compiled from the old works of such Roman horticultural writers as Varro, Columella, and Cato, but Crescenzi added his own ideas about garden matters. Soon translated into Italian, French, and German popular editions, Crescenzi's book opened up a whole new vista of gar-

Camel in Green Gets His Humps Clipped Clean. Head up, legs rooted to the ground, this topiary fantasy scans no Bactrian steppe, no burning desert sands. His world is a verdant Rhode Island garden. The California privet (*Ligustrum ovalifolium*) which gives him life comes from Japan. The art that fashioned him harks back to ancient Mediterranean lands.

Bates Littlehales,
National Geographic Photographer

dening. It was so influential that its publication can be said, so far as gardens are concerned, to mark the beginning of the Renaissance.

While the book encouraged humble and middle-class folk to have gardens if at all possible, it was the upper class and nobility who were enjoined to sponsor the building of gardens, and on a magnificent scale. The culmination of the development of the formal gardens of the Renaissance—a form based on the Roman garden—was reached in the gardens at Versailles created by André Le Nôtre for Louis XIV.

The Dutch garden was also formal. But unlike the French garden with its great vistas, it was cut up into small flower beds. Both types went to England and there the two styles were mingled. The English formal garden also usually exhibited considerable "bush barbering," or topiary work and clipped hedges. This type came to America in the colonial garden. Thus we trace the wanderings of the formal garden from Egypt to our own back yards.

Following the odyssey of the informal ornamental garden will take us farther. As we already have noted, it began in Mesopotamia. From there it went to India and on to China. Between the years 1735 and 1772 a series of books on Chinese and other Oriental gardens, written by keen observers who had been there and seen them, appeared in England. While some who tried to imitate the features described got no further than sticking mock pagodas into their gardens, others caught the spirit of the studied informality of the Chinese garden and put it to excellent use.

Coupled with greensward, this Anglo-Chinese garden became what we now call the typical English garden: a lawn surrounded by a mixed border of ornamental plants in an informal but pleasing array. This type of garden has become increasingly popular in America.

Different as are these two garden types, they still have one thing in common—the ancient

Volkmar Wentzel, National Geographic Photographer

A Flower's Fleeting Beauty Lives On in Stone. Some 300 years ago a Mogul artist graced a Delhi palace with this delicate marble inlay. Today's Indian craftsman draws on centuries-old skills to restore its jewel-like surface. Islamic belief forbidding representations of the human figure in mosques led to high development and wide use of designs based on flower, tendril, and leaf.

water supply. When gardening first began, it was noted that there were occasional periods when the plants needed water. For convenience gardens were located near a spring or pool. In spite of our hoses and sprinkler systems, we usually manage to slip the time-honored water supply into our gardens in some form. The pool will still be there, or a combination fountain and pool. The fountain here represents the original bubbling spring.

There is a pool in the garden of one friend. My other friend stoutly denies he has a pool. But it is there just the same. All he has done is to raise it into the air, put a pedestal under it, and call it a birdbath.

Californians have every reason to be proud of their patio gardens. Imitations have been attempted in the North, but they come short of expectation because the plants characterizing them usually will not stand cold. But this interesting garden type is not Californian. For that matter, it is not Mexican. It goes back much farther in man's history.

The Persian garden was carried on the crest of the wave of Moslem conquest across North Africa and ultimately into Spain, where the Moors built great gardens. The first Spanish emir, Abd-ar-Rahman, chose Cordova as his capital in the year 755. There he fashioned a garden such as he had known in his youth in Damascus. It is said that he sent agents and plant explorers from Spain as far east as Syria, to the borders of China in Turkistan, and even into India, to collect plants for this garden.

With the passing centuries the Moorish garden became an Iberian tradition, for it was not until 1492 that the last Moslem stronghold in Spain fell to Ferdinand and Isabella.

Continuing our rediscovery of the origins of the patio garden, we go back now to a fertility and blessing-of-the-crops rite celebrated among the Babylonians and Assyrians. This spread to an offshoot of this culture, to the Phoenicians. The rite was taken to Cyprus, an old Phoenician colony, and later to Greece where, about the seventh century B.C., we find it celebrated as the Adonis festival.

At first in this festival, quick-growing plants such as lettuce were put in pots. Later more

permanent and decorative plants were used. And so began the custom of raising plants in pots around the house. This custom was picked up by the Romans and taken to Spain. There it was welded into the Mohammedan garden and became the Spanish type.

When Cortés conquered Mexico, he found excellent gardens—much better, in fact, than anything at that time in Europe. But the Conquistadores destroyed these Aztec gardens, so that today only slight vestiges remain. Consequently, when the Spanish settlers and clergy began to flock to Mexico, they had to start their gardens all over again. Naturally they used the type they were most familiar with— the garden they had left behind in Spain. Thus strong elements of the Moslem garden, which fitted into the Moorish style of

architecture also brought to this hemisphere, came to Mexico. Its features were a well—the old water supply again—with small flower beds near by, a few trees, and almost always some potted plants. Padre Serra took this characteristic but simple type of patio garden from Mexico into California when he established his system of missions. And that is how the Persian garden, plus a fertility rite represented by potted plants, came to California.

A much simpler story is the origin of the rock garden. Some see its beginnings in the grottoes popular in Greek and Roman gardens, and there may indeed be a touch of grottoism in these. But the modern rock garden can be given an exact starting date.

Clusius, the old Flemish herbalist (we shall meet him later, puttering about with his tulips, page 60), became interested in Alpine plants

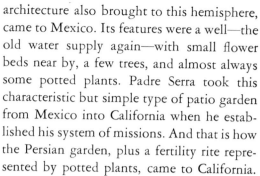

while he was in Austria. Others tried to raise this type of plant, but also without any great success. We now know that these Alpine plants require special drainage and soil conditions.

Apparently the first person to have any real success with these plants was the English botanist and plant explorer, Sir Joseph Banks. He took slabs of lava rock which he had brought back from Iceland on one of his expeditions, some old stones dumped out from repairs then being made on the Tower of London, some locally collected flints and chalk rock, as well as some broken brick. With these he constructed a "rockery" in the old Chelsea Physic Garden in 1772.

With the opening of the 18th century the intellectual ferment of the "Age of Reason" revived the ancient profession of plant explorer. From China, Japan, Ceylon, India, Australia, Africa, the Near East, from the West Indies, North America, and South America—from the whole world plants began pouring into the botanical centers of Europe. Botanists and gardeners were in a constant furor over the procession of exciting new finds. It was the Golden Age of the plant explorer, for it was a poor explorer

Green Treasure of Sierra Madre Rides the Backs of Plodding Mules. Author's party returns from slopes of Mexico's 11,138-foot Zempoaltepec (meaning "twenty peaks"). The expedition ends in Oaxaca, but its live cargo of plants and seeds moves on from discoverer to breeder and perhaps finally to you, as a new garden species. Dr. Camp has sought beautiful and useful plants far and wide.

Wendell H. Camp

1730, founded one of the first botanical gardens in America and scoured the region from Florida to Lake Erie for plants to fill it. So far as we can learn, it was Bartram in this garden who did the first controlled hybridizing of garden flowers in America.

Bartram corresponded widely with the learned botanists and best gardeners of Europe. Scarcely a boat left Philadelphia which did not contain a parcel of seed or living plants collected by him; in return, people sent him rare plants from various parts of the world. Many plants now common were first grown in America in this garden. Soon nurseries sprang up and the Philadelphia region became the garden center of North America.

Nor was the South lagging. At Charleston, Henry Laurens was introducing many exotic plants fit for that climate. At near-by Otranto, physician and naturalist Alexander Garden (the *Gardenia* was named for him) was carrying on correspondence with the great Swedish botanist Linnaeus. And it was at Charleston that André Michaux, peer of early American plant explorers, had one of his nurseries and collecting stations. Another Charlestonian, of a later period, is especially remembered during our winter holiday season, for the *Poinsettia* was introduced by and named in honor of diplomat-Congressman Joel R. Poinsett.

who did not return with a goodly portion of his findings new ones. Those of us who now poke into odd corners of the world for plants sigh for "the good old days."

On this side of the Atlantic for a long time there had been gardens scattered along the seaboard wherever settlements had sprung up. And the plant explorers were not far behind. John Clayton (for whom our spring beauty, *Claytonia*, was named) came to these shores for the first time in 1705. Men like Mark Catesby followed (he is remembered in *Lilium catesbaei*). Peter Kalm, the Swede, visited our shores and took many plants back to Europe (*Kalmia*, the mountain laurel honors his name). But to John Bartram, the Quaker plowman, we make our deepest bow.

This native of Darby (near Philadelphia) became so interested in botany that he neglected his farm, studied Latin so that he could read the early texts, and set about learning all he could about plants. It was he who, about

48

The Virginians were not behind their neighbors. Visitors to Mount Vernon can easily see in the restored garden, laid out according to the diary and notes kept by George Washington, that he was a lover of plants and a gardener of no mean ability. Thomas Jefferson, who wrote on natural history as well as on government, carried on, like Bartram, a wide scientific correspondence and introduced many new plants and garden methods at Monticello.

Other gardens were springing up. In 1801 Dr. David Hosack acquired 20 acres from the City of New York and laid out a botanical garden. The Elgin Gardens, as he called the plot, lay on what is now Fifth Avenue between 50th and 51st Streets, where Rockefeller Center stands. Roof and terrace gardens atop these modern buildings, commemorating Dr. Hosack's efforts, are reminiscent of the Hanging Gardens Nebuchadnezzar built in Babylon.

Since the days of the early Dutch, French, and English colonists, botanical gardens have been active in the discovery and development of garden materials in all parts of the world.

Large and famous private nurseries had been springing up because of the increased interest in gardens. Many of them had their own botanical explorers who brought together additional stocks of garden material. Especially in Europe, these nurseries also became the centers of hybridization and selection of new forms of ornamentals. This activity eventually came to this side of the Atlantic, and American nurserymen, with the newer techniques supplied by recent advances in the knowledge of breeding plants, are now taking the lead in this necessary and basic phase of floriculture.

Today one cannot walk into a garden without seeing on every side the results of the plant breeder's work. It is the job of the plant explorer to bring the material out of the world's far places. The hybridist and selector then work over it, sometimes for years, finally passing it on to us in the form of choice garden flowers, often quite different from what they originally were in the wild.

Some time ago Mrs. Bostelmann, already well known to me through her paintings, came into my office and asked if I would give her a list of about a hundred flowering plants commonly grown in American ornamental gardens, together with the countries of their origin. It seemed like a simple affair; that is, until I really got into the job.

Today man cultivates about 25,000 species of plants. Of these about 10,000 are cherished for their ornamental flowers. Of this latter number, several thousand might be classed as being fairly common in America.

In making up this list, we selected a representative group. The name and native country of each was put on a card, and cards were sorted by geographic origin so as to give some idea of the proportion of paintings to be devoted to each region. Further selection reduced the list to two hundred species—still twice too many. Discarding that last hundred seemed like turning one's back on one's best friends. It was sheer botanical agony.

As a last resort, certain cards were turned face downward, shuffled, and a number selected at random. If your favorite garden flower happens to have been omitted, it very likely was among those which were not pulled out of the pile. Our desire to include as many plants as possible will explain to gardeners why species with dissimilar climatic and soil requirements, or of different blooming periods, sometimes appear in the same picture.

For six months a miraculous thing happened. I simply laid out the plot. The artist planted the garden, tended it, and there on her easel plants bloomed. The following series of paintings—"Mrs. Bostelmann's garden," her friends called it—is evidence of the marvelous climate and growing conditions to be found in an artist's studio in Manhattan.

From Medieval European Gardens

THE FAR-FLUNG EMPIRE of the Caesars had at last crumbled and the *pax Romana* was a thing of the past. Political and economic chaos reigned in much of the then civilized world. Brigandage was rife. The common folk deserted their farms and crowded their cottages beneath the protecting battlements of the great castles.

During the turmoils and alarms of the "Dark Ages" many vegetables and flowers earlier introduced by the Romans were lost. Having no access to gardens of the outside world, the people of medieval Europe turned to the plants of their own woods and pastures.

The first of these garden introductions, such as the daisy, primrose, pansy, and bellflower, were purely accidental. They probably came in as weeds or with the turf used to construct rude seats beside the castle walls. Sometimes the roots of a cherished fruit tree or flowering shrub were protected by wickerwork from horses' trampling hoofs. To the drab, insanitary castle courtyard these flowers brought a welcome fragrance, gaiety, and freshness.

Although they had not heard of nutritional deficiencies, these peoples knew the value of greens in the diet. Many wild herbs also had colorful flowers and, finding their way into castle gardens, furnished both beauty and vitamins. A haunch of venison seasoned with marigold and mint, together with a rose and primrose stew, and a chopped salad of wild onions and violets, graced many a knightly feast.

POT MARIGOLD (*Calendula officinalis*): Grown originally as a potherb as well as for its supposed medicinal properties and religious connotations (whence the name Mary's Gold), the flowering heads still are occasionally used as a savory. Favorite garden forms today have large "double-flowered" yellow or orange heads.

European Weeds Became Ornamentals in Medieval Courtyards. Pot Marigolds surmount the cluster. Bellflowers rise on fragile stems. English Daisies grow in the lower left. Modern and wild Pansies occupy the center. Wild Cowslip—"Cow's-lip"—and garden Polyanthus bloom at lower right. Turf seat abuts the castle wall.

BELLFLOWER (*Campanula*, various species): The Bluebell (*C. rotundifolia*) is still common in turf and must have been introduced early. The Chimney Bellflower (*C. pyramidalis*) also came into gardens by this same accidental route. Another member of this large genus of nearly 250 species is the Canterbury Bells (*C. medium*). Today its wild form is rarely seen in gardens. Common cultivated forms are the hose-in-hose, in which the modified and enlarged calyx encloses the corolla; and the popular cup-and-saucer, whose enlarged and colored calyx is widely flared.

DAISY (*Bellis perennis*): This charming little plant, the true or English Daisy, still is a weed in European fields and meadows; many excellent garden selections are now in cultivation. Chaucer referred to this plant as the "ee of the daie," and by Ben Jonson's time it was called "Day's Eye."

PANSY or HEARTSEASE (*Viola tricolor*): Our garden Pansy was derived from Europe's weedy "three-colored violet"; hence the scientific name, *Viola tricolor*. Several other species, through hybridization, have likely contributed to its modern forms. The English words "pansy" and "pensive" come from the French word *pensée*.

PRIMROSE (*Primula*, various species): Such species as the Field Primrose (*P. vulgaris*), the Oxlip (*P. elatior*), and the Cowslip (*P. veris*) are common in European pastures and also must have been brought in with the sods from which turf seats were made. The wild, yellowish-flowered Cow's-lip (not Cow-slip as most of us pronounce it) is shown opposite. With it is a plant now more often grown, the garden Polyanthus, derived from hybrids of the Field Primrose, the Cowslip, and the Oxlip.

ROSE (*Rosa*, various species): At least three wild species were available to medieval Europeans—the French Rose (*R. gallica*), the Dog Rose (*R. canina*), and the Eglantine or Sweetbrier (*R. eglanteria*). The last was enshrined in song and story (page 26). The Rose was valued for food before its beauty was appreciated. The fruits, we now know, are rich in vitamins.

European Meadows and Our Lawns

WHEN WE TRACE PLANTS such as those shown opposite back to their ancestral forms, we find that millions of years ago they were neither bulbous plants nor spring bloomers. Instead, they usually were plants of the equable Tropics, which either were overtaken by large-scale climatic changes in their original home or ventured into areas where climatic conditions were seasonally unfavorable.

Eventually storage mechanisms developed— bulbs among them—enabling the plants to tide themselves over unfavorable seasons. But what if the next period favorable to growth were too brief to permit production of a complete set of leaves and flowers and to bring fruit and seed to full maturity?

For untold millions of years natural experimentation went on. Plants which had acquired the bulbous habit frequently solved the problem by telescoping operations. Leaves and flowers for the next season are produced at the end of this season's growth and packed tightly within the bulb's protective covering before the plant becomes dormant. Cut carefully through a large tulip or hyacinth bulb and you can easily see these preformed parts. They are so nearly complete that little more is needed than for the storage part of the bulb to pump water into them and blow them up to full size.

Of the plants shown, the Crocus, a member of the Iris family, is perhaps the most easily naturalized in lawns. But care should be taken that we do not get the lawnmower out too early. For some weeks after the flowers have passed, the leaves are busy manufacturing the food necessary to produce next year's flowers.

SPRING CROCUS (*Crocus vernus*): Of the nearly 75 species, this native of southern and central Europe is the one most commonly planted. Found in profusion in Alpine meadows, it is perhaps more at home in our northern lawns than other species native in the Mediterranean region or western Asia. But it is not unusual to see sprinkled across a lawn the infiltrating yellow tints of the Balkan Crocus (*C. moesiacus*— meaning "from the land of the Moesians," or Balkans), or the Cloth-of-gold Crocus (*C. susi-*

anus), a native of the Crimea introduced into modern culture from gardens of the ancient city of Susa in Persia.

"Crocus" is the Greek name of the Saffron, another species. Unlike the more familiar plants of this genus, the Saffron (*Crocus sativus*) blooms in autumn. The small, three-branched styles in the center of the flower are gathered as a source of saffron, long used both as a textile dye and a condiment in Asia Minor.

SNAKES-HEAD or CHECKERED-LILY (*Fritillaria meleagris*): Perhaps 70 species of Fritillary are scattered around the world in the North Temperate regions, some native in North America. Possibly because of its long domestication, the European species shown here seems to do as well as any in our gardens. The shape of its curiously mottled flowers led to the generic name, derived from *fritillus*, a dice box. The specific name, *meleagris,* means "speckled like a guinea hen." The Fritillaries belong to the Lily family; we shall encounter a different species in our Persian garden (page 63).

SNOWDROP (*Galanthus nivalis*): This impatient little member of the Amaryllis family is not to be trusted as a seasonal indicator. It is likely to push up during any warmish spell after mid-January, just in time to get itself covered with snow. Hence its specific name, *nivalis*, which means snowy. Sometimes confused with the Snowdrop is a similar garden species, the Snowflake (*Leucojum vernum*), of the same plant family, and likewise a native of Europe. But the Snowdrop's flowering stem is solid, and the three inner flower segments are much shorter than the three outer ones; while the Snowflake's flowering stem is hollow, and its six flower segments are essentially alike.

Spring's Magic Touch Brings Winter's Dormant Bulbs to Glorious Blossom in an Alpine Meadow. Blue and yellow Spring Crocus (left) leap full-blown from storage mechanisms in which they have hibernated. Snakes-Head (center) bears the descriptive alias, Checkered-Lily. Right: Snowdrop, an early bloomer.

Europe Contributed Flowers and Words

EUROPEAN LANGUAGES changed and developed as ideas and vocabularies enlarged through broader contacts with other peoples. Yet the often greatly modified names for familiar objects still contained word roots derived from folklore and ancient uses. Thus the modern names of many of our common garden plants reflect the sources of the names themselves.

FOXGLOVE (*Digitalis purpurea*): So popular is this garden plant with its dramatic spikes of varied-color flowers that we sometimes forget it is the age-old source of the medicine, digitalis. Old English folklore gave this plant its fanciful name, *Foxes glōfa*.

STOCK or GILLIFLOWER (*Matthiola incana*): In its wild form this species is a coarse shrubby perennial with single reddish or dull purplish flowers. Through years of selecting, another form is now usually grown. This is the variety *annua*, or Ten-week-stock, which comes in various colors and degrees of doubling. The name Stock, which seems only a few centuries old, probably derived from a fancied resemblance of the stiffly flared petals to the distinctive collars called stocks which men used to wear.

The plant's other name, Gilliflower, has a much longer history. We first pick it up in the Greek as *karyóphyllon* or "carinate-leaf," a name applied to some plant (possibly the progenitor of our modern Carnation) whose "leaves were shaped like the keel of a boat." The Romans conquered the Greeks and absorbed many of their words. This one they applied to plants with similar leaves. When Roman legionaries marched into Gaul, carrying the equivalent Latin word with them, it was taken up by the native peoples, further modified, and applied to various plants, among them what we now call the Clove Pink

Thatched Roof and Garden Made the 19th Century European Cottage Complete. Tallest flower is Foxglove, source of digitalis. Double garden Stocks come next. Lower center: the reddish, wild form of Stock. Right: Wallflower. At either lower margin grows Sweet Scabious, reminder of an unwashed period in our past.

or Carnation, the Wallflower, and the Stock.

The original Greek name had been so changed by its passage through classical Latin into common everyday Latin, and from there into early French, it had become Giroflée. With a curious transposition of the "r" and "l," the word got into England as Gilofre. Later this became Gilofer. As the language developed, Gilofer changed, probably into Giloflor, then Giliflour, and finally Gilliflower, which, in its modern English compound form, means nothing at all. But it does serve as a reminder of the curious routes through which so many of our English words have come to us.

WALLFLOWER (*Cheiranthus cheiri*): Originally a native of southern Europe where the climate is seasonally warm and dry, this little weed did not favor the cooler and moister soils to the north. But when man began to build houses, castles, and earthworks whose walls afforded sunny nooks where it could flourish, the Wallflower migrated northward. It now is cultivated in various colors, also in double-flowered forms.

Both the Stock and Wallflower are members of the Mustard, or Crucifer family. The word "crucifer" refers to the crosslike appearance of the four petals of the usual wild type.

"Mustard" traces back to when this ancient condiment, derived from yet another member of this large family of plants, was prepared by mixing it with "must," or new, unfermented wine.

SWEET SCABIOUS (*Scabiosa atropurpurea*): Only three of this species' many colors are shown: the blue, deep red, and pink. The deep purple (almost black) forms are often called Mourning Brides. The plant is sometimes called Pincushionflower, but the old name Scabious still seems to be preferred, a linguistic legacy of that lusty period when bathing was both a luxury and a social affectation. An old European garden was incomplete without its plot of Scabious; the flowers may have been pretty, but the plant was more valued as a cure for the "scabious," or itch.

Here in this charming modern garden plant we have another link with language of the past.

The Mediterranean Region Has Many "Bulbs"

FROM ABUNDANT EVIDENCES of ancient man found there, much of North Africa's arid wasteland apparently was once a well-watered region supporting a sizable population. The Mediterranean basin was then a broad valley formed by a slow down-buckling of earth's crust, geologists tell us. Long before the dawn of written history—not less than 10,000, but probably not more than 25,000 years ago—the Atlantic Ocean spilled over and filled this natural basin, thus creating the Mediterranean Sea.

What manner of people inhabited this valley prior to the Great Flood we may never know, but those who lived around its rim left enough clues in their rubbish heaps to give us some insight into their everyday lives.

They domesticated some of the animals they formerly had hunted. Probably first was the dog, once a hunting companion but later an assistant in herding. Goats and sheep they had as well as cows. They also harvested and tilled, for they knew wheat, barley, millet, and peas. Flax was grown for fiber.

Their leafy vegetables we know only by inference. One member of the Mustard family has been cultivated so long it has differentiated into kale, brussels sprouts, cabbage, cauliflower, broccoli, and kohlrabi—all garden varieties of *Brassica oleracea*, still found wild in its primitive form on northern cliffs rimming this old valley (page 122).

Following the advent of vegetable growing came the cultivation of flowers. Our first glimpses of ancient Egypt's great civilization reveal that these people were already expert gardeners. Funeral wreaths found in tombs indicate they grew the Lily, Cornflower, Mignonette, and Narcissus; their carvings and paintings show many more.

Other centers of Mediterranean culture arose. Gardens bloomed at Cnossus in Crete and at

Tyre; the Greeks and early Carthaginians grew flowers; the Romans took up ornamental gardening. These civilizations have long since perished and their monuments mostly turned to rubble; yet the flowers nurtured by those ancient floriculturists lived on, eventually to find their way, much changed in form, into our gardens.

Like all regions with considerable seasonal fluctuation in moisture, the Mediterranean area is rich in bulbous plants. Bulbous forms are most common in the Lily family (opposite) and the Amaryllis family, whose members there include the Jonquil and the Poets Narcissus.

GRAPE-HYACINTH (*Muscari*, various species): The 40 or more wild species, most abundant in the Mediterranean region, range eastward into Asia Minor and beyond. One, *Muscari botryoides*, a native of Mediterranean Europe, has made itself at home in our gardens and frequently escapes into lawns and waste places.

STAR-OF-BETHLEHEM (*Ornithogalum*, various species): The Ornithogalums probably were introduced into cultivation as casual but pretty weeds in vegetable plots. It is a large genus, with about 100 species in various parts of the Old World. The true Star-of-Bethlehem, *O. umbellatum*, native around the Mediterranean, is now widespread and often escapes to become a pestiferous weed.

COMMON HYACINTH (*Hyacinthus orientalis*): The 30 or more species of Hyacinth are scattered mainly from the Mediterranean region into tropical and South Africa. It is not clear, when Linnaeus christened our species, whether he thought it was from eastern Asia or from Asia Minor, in those days sometimes called the Orient. Actually, it seems to be native from Greece eastward into Asia. Probably originally purplish, the Common Hyacinth now comes in many colors. Roman Hyacinth, botanically known as *Hyacinthus orientalis* variety *albulus*, may be light blue as well as white. Its striking blooms make it especially popular for winter forcing. It is said to be native westward of the basic species from Italy into southern France.

A Garden Ruin Recalls the Floral Legacies of Dead Mediterranean Civilizations. Grape-Hyacinth (left) looks like a miniature cluster of grapes. Beside it, Star-of-Bethlehem escapes to become a weed. Roman Hyacinth (center) and Common Hyacinth (right) complete the picture. All belong to the Lily family.

Other Mediterranean Species

BY THE TIME of the Emperor Trajan (A. D. 98–117) the expanding Roman Empire reached from Britain into Africa and eastward to Egypt, the Persian Gulf, and the Caspian Sea. Its commerce brought tin from Cornish mines and other metals from Spain. Asia was tapped by camel caravan through Persia. And each year fleets set sail from an Egyptian Red Sea port for India and Ceylon, to return six months later laden with the wonders of the Orient. Carried overland by camel train to the Nile, thence downriver to Alexandria, those precious cargoes were transshipped and sent on to Rome.

Before the stirring days of Julius Caesar the Romans had gardens of sorts, yet even as late as the time of Pliny the Younger (A. D. *c.* 62–113), the strictly ornamental plants were limited mainly to natives of adjacent regions. But Roman legionaries had seen the strange plants and floral displays of Egypt and Asia Minor, and their leaders coveted such gardens.

With the building of great estates and public parks, growing wealth and commerce brought plants from faraway places to Rome. In turn, Roman officials took garden materials to distant parts of the Empire with them, thus introducing many exotics to western Europe.

For three centuries after the time of Pliny horticulture developed, and Rome became a city of magnificent gardens. As the city grew congested, vacation residences were built. Terraced villas overlooking the blue Mediterranean became fashionable throughout the Empire.

Meanwhile the peoples to the north were growing restless. In the year 410, Alaric the Goth marched through Italy and captured Rome. Later the Vandals left Spain, took Carthage, and in A. D. 455 sacked Rome.

The abandoned gardens and villas fell into disrepair. Most of the exotic plants perished, not to be reintroduced for almost a thousand years. Except for a few pockets of culture (the Arabs were developing their own style of gardening, which was later introduced into Spain), ornamental gardening around the European edge of the Mediterranean during the "Dark Ages" was almost limited to species, such as the following, which were native there.

OLEANDER (*Nerium oleander*): This shrub, hardy in the South, is often grown indoors in the North to be set out in the summer. The botanical name combines two very old ones. *Nerium* is its Greek name. *Oleander* is a Roman folk-name and refers to the resemblance of the leaves to those of the olive tree or *olea*, its name in classical Latin. Our word "oil" stems from the same root word.

SNAPDRAGON (*Antirrhinum majus*): Press the sides of one of these flowers and the two lips snap open; hence the English common name. The name *Antirrhinum* comes from the Greek and means "shaped like a nose."

CANDYTUFT (*Iberis*, various species): The 35 or so species of Candytuft are scattered around the Mediterranean region. The dwarfish annual, white-flowered Rocket Candytuft, *I. amara* (from *amarus*, referring to its bitter flavor), may become weedy. The closely related *I. umbellata* (in reference to its flower cluster) is larger and comes in shades of rose, red, and purple. Another group of species represented in our picture by *I. sempervirens* is perennial and evergreen ("sempervirens"); others of this group come in varying colors. *Iberis* derives from the ancient name for Spain, source of several cultivated species.

The English common name does not refer to something to eat but is a corruption of Candé (Candia), ancient name for the island of Crete, where another species is native; hence the "tufted plant from Candé," or "Candétuft."

On the terrace are two other Mediterranean plants often grown in warm regions. One is the Italian Stone Pine, *Pinus pinea*, source of commercial European "pine nuts" used as food. The other is the True Aloe, *Aloe vera*. The juice from its succulent leaves has recently been found helpful in treating X-ray burns.

The Romans Abandoned Their Seaside Villas, but Native Plants Persisted. Candytuft, at the lower left margin, looks up at Snapdragon and Oleander (top). The fleshy-leaved plants with yellow spikes on the terrace are True Aloes. Above, an Italian Stone Pine, source of "pine nuts," spreads its branches.

Turkey and the Tulip

THE GARDENERS OF ASIA MINOR long have favored the tulip, for its culture is admirably fitted to their short springs tucked between bleak winters and parched summers. The fifty or so known wild species are scattered from the Mediterranean region eastward into Asia, and wherever they grow wild they have been brought into cultivation. But it was Turkey's early gardeners who made the best collections, hybridized and selected them, and started the tulip on its way into our gardens.

The later trail of the plants is fairly clear. Busbequius, Austrian ambassador at the court of the Sultan of Turkey, there saw and admired the tulip and brought seed back to Vienna in 1554. From 1573 to 1587 the herbalist Clusius was court gardener to Maximilian II at Vienna, where he must have come into contact with the plant. Later Clusius was professor at the University of Leiden in Holland (he died in 1609) and it was he who introduced a fine collection and popularized the tulip in that country.

Tulips became the rage in Holland by the early 1630's. Spirited bidding for bulbs of newly developed varieties grew into wild speculation between 1634 and 1637. (When the Dutch government finally clamped down, certain rare bulbs sold for as much as $10,000 apiece.) But from this period of "tulipomania" an honorable industry evolved.

During World War II, food-short Hollanders reportedly were reduced to eating tulip bulbs. They must be prepared carefully, with knowledge that certain types contain an alkaloid poison; but "safe" kinds once were used as food.

TULIP: We grow today two general classes, the "garden" and "species" tulips. Briefly this means that garden tulips have been so hybridized that this group will not "come true" if raised from seed, whereas species tulips, nearer the wild types, will come true from seed. The differentiation no longer is completely valid, though still used. *Tulipa kaufmanniana* and *T. clusiana* (named for Clusius) have long been favorites in the species class.

The garden tulips are of various types. Among the earliest-blooming are the Duc van Thol group, thought perhaps to derive mainly from *Tulipa suaveolens*. The graceful "cottage" type (long grown around European cottages) and the more recent Darwin tulips (honoring Charles Darwin) are classified as *Tulipa gesneriana*. Their real origin, however, seems to be shrouded in the mystery of the various unknown wild forms brought together and hybridized in the early Turkish gardens.

"Breeder" tulips also are offered for sale; some consider them a distinct group. Historically, however, the term "breeder" was applied to a self-color tulip (that is, to a tulip having a single color with no stripes, markings, or marginal frills and produced directly by hybridization). Also, it is this type which is usually used in further hybridization or breeding.

Tulips are subject to a nonfatal infection of a plant virus which sometimes causes the solid color to break up into stripes and variegated markings. For example, the parti-colored Rembrandt group is merely the result of a series of virus breaks which have occurred in various members of the single-colored breeders of the Darwin type. Now that the cause of this once mysterious phenomenon is known, it is possible to produce such variegated forms. Another group is the bizarre "parrot" type; these are tulips of the *gesneriana* section with curiously frilled and often multi-colored parts.

It has been impossible to present anything like a representative sample of the multitude of garden and species tulips offered in the trade. You will no doubt select bulbs through the colored pictures in the catalogues anyway, where the classes and varieties will be fully named. In each, the word "tulip" was derived from a word meaning turban—enough to remind us that turbaned Turks of centuries ago started them on the long road to our gardens.

Long Before Holland, Turkey Cultivated the Tulip. Various "garden" types are depicted, the more unusual being the bizarre, multicolored parrot Tulip (left); several "species" Tulips (center); and, toward the right with reflexed parts, an early garden form. The name "tulip" stems from a word meaning turban.

"In a Persian Garden"

WITH THE STEADY INCREASE in aridity through-out western Asia during the last 5,000 years or more, the peoples of this region more and more had to depend on irrigation for success with their plants. Pleasure plots of trees and flowers of necessity were restricted in size. This led to experimentation on the most economical spacing of plants and on combinations of species so that no part of a garden would long be devoid of bloom. Concentration on these details raised the art of gardening to a high level.

Religion, as it has elsewhere, played an important part in directing the trend of garden practices in western Asia. Those who held to the ancient faith of Zoroaster firmly believed that heaven was a garden or paradise. And the much later teachings of Mohammed did nothing to dispel this faith; in fact, Mohammed increased the number of heavenly gardens. In addition to sparkling fountains, shade trees, and banks of fragrant flowers, it was promised the faithful that one of these Persian paradises would have attendants "with complexions like rubies and pearls"; another, brunettes "with fine black eyes."

To the old Persian, a garden and paradise were the same thing. And that is why Omar the Tentmaker could pay no prettier compliment to his ladylove than to say that if she would but sit beside him singing in the wilderness it would be paradise enough.

One thing the Koran forbade; that was the making of images. Therefore the gardens of the Mohammedan period were neither cluttered with statuary nor tortured with examples of clipped topiary work. The Persians' innate love of design and form was reflected in the intricate patterns of the garden itself. Usually rectangular in shape, the garden almost invariably centered around a well, or storage pool. Generally four main paths met at the well, these bordered by canals. From these the smaller irrigation channels in turn led directly to the various plots. Because of this necessary irrigation system in a relatively small space, the entire garden became geometric in form.

But those bleak Persian winters and the clammy tile floors of the homes! What, then, would be more natural than to cover these chilly tiles with warm rugs "when the rose is dead and the last bird flown"? We can easily imagine some aged satrap ordering his rug weavers to make a copy of his beloved summer garden, to bring him winter comfort and pleasure.

Such old Persian rugs may still be seen in museums. In execution they are complete even, in some, to individual trees and flowering plants of recognizable species. Later these lesser details became stylized parts of the general geometric pattern.

Many modern rugs made on mechanical looms still retain the basic design of a central well with the four main paths. One type of rug border represents the tiled or pebble-strewn path around the garden. Another border design recalls the original pattern of trees and rose arbors which bounded the garden.

Of the many flowers the Persians grew, two, both native to Persian hills, are shown opposite.

CROWN IMPERIAL (*Fritillaria imperialis*): Lifting its crown of green leaves to the height of two or three feet, this bulbous member of the Lily family is a striking plant when in bloom. Originally the flowers were a rather dull yellowish red, but deep brick-red and almost yellow garden forms are now known.

ORIENTAL POPPY (*Papaver orientale*): In the wild state, this showy and easily grown perennial has scarlet flowers with black centers. Garden forms now come in various patterns and colors, some derived by hybridization with *Papaver bracteatum*, another species which occurs wild in Persia. Unlike other species of garden poppy, this group can be propagated from root cuttings. Many handsome named varieties are offered by the trade.

The Gardener's Quartered Paradise Gave Its Design to the Persian Rug. To endure winter's cold, ancient Iranians sought comfort in carpets woven in geometric pattern to resemble summer's gardens with a well in the center. Here Crown Imperial lifts its showy head above scarlet and white Oriental Poppies.

The Dutch and South Africa

THE DUTCH EAST INDIA COMPANY was chartered in the year 1602 to open up trade between Holland and the Far East, via the Cape of Good Hope. In 1648 the *Haarlem*, a ship of the Company, was wrecked in Table Bay near what is now Cape Town. Fortunately saving a little seed, the survivors raised a small garden in the five months before their rescue.

Scurvy was then common on long voyages. The shipwrecked sailors, who had no inkling that vitamin deficiency was the cause, nonetheless realized that occasional fruits and green vegetables kept them healthier. On their return to Holland they urged that a garden be established at this halfway place where passing ships' crews could get fresh foods. Two ships' companies left Holland in 1652 for this purpose.

Landing at Table Bay, they built a fort and laid out a soon-flourishing garden. Their gardeners were interested also in the unknown plants they found growing naturally about them, and moved many into odd corners of the vegetable plots.

And so began the real cultivation of the plants of South Africa, destined for an important part in the growth of modern ornamental gardening. By 1679 the original garden included ornamental materials from upcountry regions of Africa as well as edible and ornamental materials brought by sea from China, Java, Zanzibar, and other points along the way. As early as 1700 these plants from Table Bay were common in Holland; they later found their way to gardens elsewhere in the world.

CALLA (*Zantedeschia aethiopica*): For convenience this plant has been called Calla, following frequent usage; but the name really belongs to another member of the same family, *Calla palustris*, a delightful little plant of our northern swamps and bog gardens. More often it is called Calla-Lily, but this is worse. The plant is not a lily; it belongs to the Arum family, along with our lowly Skunk Cabbage, Jack-in-the-Pulpit, Elephant's-Ear, Taro, Caladium, and more than 1,500 other species.

Also, the showy thing which looks like a flower is actually a highly modified leaf surrounding a central spike on which are found the numerous small, closely packed flowers. Despite the confusion in names, the Calla is one of Africa's best contributions to our gardens. Several other species with silver-spotted leaves, or with reddish or yellow spathes, are also grown. The genus was named for Francesco Zantedeschi, an Italian student of plants of over a century ago.

BIRD-OF-PARADISE FLOWER (*Strelitzia reginae*): At first sight one of these bizarre plants in bloom is a botanical puzzle. The several flowers on each stem are enclosed by a much modified, boat-shaped leaf and come popping up one after another. The three sepals of each flower are yellow, or in cultivated forms sometimes orangey. There are also three petals, one very small. The other two have been modified, swung forward into line, and form the blue "tongue"; in its groove lie the ends of the reproductive structures. This plant, a not-too-distant relative of the banana, was named in honor of Queen Charlotte Sophia, of the house of Mecklenburg-Strelitz, wife of George III.

IMPATIENS (*Impatiens holsti*): A native of tropical East Africa, this increasingly popular plant originally had brick-red flowers. Using its more vigorous and rapid growth, earlier blooming habit, and larger flowers as a base, hybridists have now given this species a wider range of tints, ranging from scarlet to salmon, pink, and white, by hybridizing it with the otherwise less desirable *Impatiens sultani* of Zanzibar. This species is taking the place of the old Garden Balsam, *Impatiens balsamina*, a native of tropical Asia, which unfortunately hides its flowers under the leaves. Anyone who has pinched a ripe fruit pod of this group knows why the genus was named *Impatiens*.

Shipwreck and Scurvy Fastened World Attention on Africa's Rich Flora. Dutch navigators, who established a garden at Table Bay to combat scurvy, began the introduction of African plants into Europe and thence to the world almost three centuries ago. Calla (top), Impatiens (right), and Bird-of-Paradise Flower (center).

A "Jolly Botanical Band" from Africa

WHEN JOHN HUTCHINSON, former Keeper of Museums of Botany, Royal Botanic Gardens, Kew, England, recorded his travels in the book *A Botanist in Southern Africa*, he was fortunate indeed in having so distinguished a friend and expedition companion to write its foreword.

I quote from this foreword by the late soldier, statesman, and enthusiastic student of plants, Field Marshal the Right Honorable Dr. Jan Christiaan Smuts, then Prime Minister of the Union of South Africa:

"What a jolly botanical band we were! . . . What busy days of collecting, swimming the rivers, climbing the mountains; nights by the veld fire, with the native dances to the beating of Africa drums; sleeping under the stars . . . ; camping by the ruins of Zimbabwe, by the smoke-mist of the Victoria Falls, by the shores of Lake Tanganyika and the banks of the Luanzua torrent rushing headlong into it. What joy to find plants never found before . . . ! It was a thrilling time, and some of us were invited into the mysteries of Africa in an experience which will surely never be forgotten."

What a "jolly botanical band" indeed! And how the good Dr. Smuts and his friend Hutchinson are to be envied this exciting hunt for the remarkable plants of Africa.

POKER-PLANT (*Kniphofia*, several species): Of the more than 50 available species of this tropical and South African genus, the large-flowered *K. uvaria* and the small-flowered *K. foliosa* are the types most often grown. These species are not likely to be found now in their original forms in gardens, for they have been hybridized with others of the genus and show considerable variation. The reddish forms are often called Red-hot-pokers or Torch-flowers. This genus belongs to the Lily family.

Africa's Sun Brings Brilliant Colors. The Continent's "mysteries" include botanical secrets yet undiscovered. These species, however, are well known. Poker-Plant holds its flower spike erect. Gerbera blooms on the left. Lower center: Lobelia; right: Cape Marigold. Castor oil comes from beanlike seeds of "tree" beside village wall.

GERBERA (*Gerbera jamesoni*): Originally found with predominantly orange heads, this spectacular member of the Sunflower family has been broken up into many different color forms, examples of which are pictured toward the left.

CAPE MARIGOLD (*Dimorphotheca aurantiaca*): Among the 20-odd species in this group of showy South African plants, some are annuals, some perennial herbs, and still others are shrubby. In our northern gardens this popular species comes into flower soon enough so that it can be treated as an annual; farther south, where frost does not touch it, some strains persist and become somewhat shrubby. Thought originally to be yellow or orange, the flower heads of this species now exhibit a wide color range, likely the result of hybridization with the more variably colored *D. annua*.

LOBELIA (*Lobelia erinus*): There is scarcely a region in the world where one is not likely to stumble on one or more of the 250 species of Lobelia known to botanists. In color they range from red, orange, and yellowish to violet, blue, and even white. Our native American Cardinal-Flower (*L. cardinalis*) exemplifies one red end of this floral spectrum. The dwarfish species seem to run more to blues, and this South African species (*L. erinus*) is no exception. It was originally a rather diffuse and untidy plant, but numerous low, compact, and floriferous forms have been selected, making it today one of our most effective plants for edgings. Varieties may be had in deep or light blue, purple, rose, crimson, or white. Foliage ranges from pale to deep green, with some forms bronze- or red-tinged.

CASTOR-OIL-PLANT (*Ricinus communis*): This primarily economic plant is also popular as an ornamental. In rich soil it grows rapidly and brings a truly exotic note into our northern gardens. In the frost-free Tropics the plants grow treelike, up to 40 feet high. The stem and leaf vary somewhat in color; in Mexico, where the plant is grown commercially, the forms with red-streaked, deeply divided leaves are called *palmacristi*—Palm of Christ.

More Africans, "Brought Back Alive"

THE PLANT HUNTER is fortunate in many ways. Unlike the animal collector, his "game" does not require elaborate traps. Furthermore, instead of hiding furtively it often waves its multicolored banners in the air, seemingly to attract his attention.

FRINGED HIBISCUS (*Hibiscus schizopetalus*): The usually sparse branches and scattered leaves of this East African shrub of themselves would scarcely seem attractive enough for our frost-free gardens. Also, the flowers admittedly are not abundant. But when even one of those buds, swaying on its long, pendent stalk, swells up and bursts open, the result is recompense enough for having carefully tended the plant.

PELARGONIUM or "GERANIUM" (*Pelargonium*, various species): There are upward of 250 species in the genus *Pelargonium*, most occurring in South Africa. Although popularly termed Geraniums, this group actually should have another name. *Geranium* comes from the Greek word for crane and refers to the shape of the fruit; the true geraniums are often called Cranesbill.

Many of us are familiar with the common woodland *Geranium maculatum*, which sometimes is cultivated successfully, and the even more familiar garden plant, *Geranium sanguineum*, a native of Eurasia. *Pelargonium* was derived from the Greek word for stork; again, the shape of the fruit has led to the common name, Storksbill. Although similar in appearance, there is sufficient technical difference between the flowers of *Geranium* and *Pelargonium* for botanists—and many gardeners—to keep the species in separate genera.

Some species of wild Pelargoniums have ventured into the semidesert areas of South Africa and there taken on coarse, clubby, even spiny stems, looking much like cacti. Also, like cacti, some desert Pelargoniums have almost lost their leaves; the thickened green stems have taken over the function of leaves and also act as water-storage organs. Other species which favored moister conditions became leafy, trailing, or scrambling vinelike plants.

Many of the erect-growing leafy species have a strong odor, leading to such names as Apple-, Rose-, Lemon-, and Nutmeg-Geraniums (or Pelargoniums!). Because of considerable hybridization in the past, it now is extremely difficult to decide just which of the wild species were ancestral to our cultivated forms. The most frequently grown today is the Fish-Pelargonium, the geranium of pot and window-box culture. In its many color phases it is also an effective bedding-out plant. In southern Florida and California it will grow year after year, forming great woody plants which, if carefully pruned and trained, can be made to cover fences and trellises.

GLADIOLUS (*Gladiolus*, various species): The 200 or more species of this important garden group are scattered from the Mediterranean southward, the greatest concentration being in the Cape region. Like *Pelargonium*, the genus *Gladiolus* has been a fertile field for the hybridist. Today they come in a wide variety of forms and colors; none looks very much like the original species. When Linnaeus christened this genus about 200 years ago, he did not have our modern showy-flowered plants to study. Apparently more impressed with the shape of the swordlike leaves, he used the name *Gladiolus*, from the Latin, meaning little sword. The word "gladiator" comes from the same base.

AFRICAN-VIOLET (*Saintpaulia ionantha*): This charming blue-flowered plant was named for its discoverer, Baron Walter von Saint Paul. It may be grown from seed but usually is propagated from leaf cuttings. Although Africa has native true violets, this is not one of them; the African—or Usambara—"Violet" belongs to the Gesneria family.

"Darkest Africa" Enriched the World's Gardens with These Radiant Blooms. Pelargonium, often mistakenly called Geranium, peeps in from the left. Gladiolus (center) was named for its swordlike leaves. Fringed Hibiscus (right) swings like a pendulum. Popular African-Violet (below) is not a true violet.

Plant Marvels of Madagascar

BROWSING THROUGH certain "travel" books of a century or more ago, written mostly from hearsay and legend, the reader stumbles upon weird fables such as: "Madagascar, home of the Poison-gas-bush; a shrub which exhales so insidiously poisonous a vapor that birds, merely flying through its branches, fall dead." Or, "Mysterious Madagascar, land of the voracious strangler-tree; a tree whose prehensile branches quickly encircle the unwary passers-by, holding and crushing them until they die; then the tree slowly proceeds to devour the victims, leaving only bleached and whitened bones."

Naturally, plant explorers long ago exploded these myths. Even so, Madagascar is a land full of botanical surprises. Unfortunately, relatively few are amenable to garden culture.

FLAMBOYANT or ROYAL POINCIANA

(*Delonix regia*): Being sensitive to frost, this magnificent flowering tree is mainly a plant of the Tropics; yet it is commonly found in gardens, parks, and along the streets in southern Florida and California. Some years ago when I lived in Haiti there was an old Flamboyant beside the house, a gnarled relic of French colonial days. Seemingly overnight its contorted branches burst into what looked like scarlet-orange flame.

One day as I stood wondering at its sheer magnificence, a flock of small birds came tumbling out of the sky and settled among the gorgeous flowers. I recognized them as warblers hurrying northward by way of Caribbean island steppingstones from winter homes in the South American jungles. After catching their breath (and a good meal of insects) the warblers flew on toward the cool forests of New England and Canada. The old Flamboyant stayed behind, as it had for countless other springtimes, nodding

Madagascar, Land of Botanical Surprises, Yields These Three Exotics. When thirsty Madagascans tap the fan-shaped Travelers-Tree, a pint of water wells from each leaf base. Crown-of-Thorns, linked in legend with Biblical events, has spiny stems. Flamboyant Tree spreads in the distance; its blossoms are shown close-up at top.

drowsily in the Haitian sun, almost as if dreaming of its real home on the faraway, hot plains of Madagascar.

CROWN-OF-THORNS

(*Euphorbia mili; E. splendens* of florists): This species is grown as a pot plant in winter, to be set outside in the summer months. In our southern gardens, protected from frost, it joins other decorative, sun-loving plants. The gray spiny stems with their few green leaves would be interesting alone, but the pert scarlet or orange-crimson "flowers" are the real attraction. I use the word "flowers" cautiously; in all Euphorbias, the objects which look like petals in reality are bracts, highly modified and sometimes gaudily colored leaves surrounding the real flowers. We meet an even showier Euphorbia in the Mexican Poinsettia (page 89).

The Crown-of-Thorns in legend is supposed to have played a part in the humiliation of Christ before His crucifixion. We therefore find artists including this plant in Biblical scenes. Although found today in gardens of the Holy Land, there are reasons to doubt its presence there 1,900 years ago.

Botanically unwary artists also often include cacti when painting the rough and thorny paths trod by the saints and prophets of old. The cacti are wholly American and, like the Crown-of-Thorns, were introduced into Palestinian gardens. Finding suitable climate there, they since have escaped from cultivation and now appear to be parts of the native flora.

TRAVELERS-TREE

(*Ravenala madagascariensis*): Because of its curious appearance and remarkable two-ranked leaves, the Travelers-Tree is grown in many of our frost-free gardens. It is related to the Strelitzias (a species of which appears on page 65) though its flowers are not so showy. The common name of this plant suggests its use, for, if a hole is bored through a leaf base near the stem, up to a pint of reasonably good drinking water wells out. The Flamboyant, the Crown-of-Thorns, and the Travelers-Tree—truly an exotic trio from faraway Madagascar, land of botanical surprises!

From Tropical Southeastern Asia

MAN, FROM MANY EVIDENCES, has lived in tropical southeastern Asia for a very long time. In the jungles of Cambodia, Burma, and elsewhere ancient temple ruins indicate a once-great civilization. Yet even before these temples were built, the peoples of southeastern Asia and adjacent islands had been cultivating plants for thousands of years.

When history first opens on these peoples, they had already found and developed such basic food plants as rice, sugar cane, various beans, the eggplant, cucumber, taro, yam (the true yam, not the sweet potato), plantain, and coconut. They had such fruits as the banana, pomelo (the ancestor of our grapefruit), and mango. The three highly ornamental plants opposite all seem to have been associated with the peoples of southeastern Asia first as foods.

EAST INDIAN LOTUS (*Nelumbium nelumbo*): This majestic water-lily goes under many erroneous names, one of the most frequent being "Egyptian Lotus." The real Egyptian Lotus is a different plant, with large *floating* leaves; botanically, a species of *Nymphaea*. Even this plant is wrongly named, for the fruits supposed to have been eaten by the *lōtophágoi*, or Lotus-eaters of Greek legend, did not come from the "Egyptian Lotus" but from a shrub apparently of the Cyrenaican coast on the south shore of the Mediterranean. It seems rather a pity that we invent all sorts of silly names for this plant when we have a perfectly good one in the botanical name *nelumbo*, derived from its native name in Ceylon.

The early primitive peoples of southeastern Asia first cultivated the plant for its large tuberous rootstocks and the nutlike seeds; both still are used as food. Appreciation of the plant for its beauty probably came only after the rise of

the great Asiatic cultures and their interest in growing flowers. It now grows in Egypt, but seems to have been introduced there from tropical Asia by ancient Romans to combat famine.

HIBISCUS (*Hibiscus*, several species): The red flower shown is *Hibiscus rosa-sinensis*, or Rose-of-China. Its buds still are used in curries and soups. Early travelers found this plant growing in the gardens of southern Cathay and other parts of southeastern Asia and prized it for its beauty. Much later the East African Fringed Hibiscus, *H. schizopetalus* (page 68), was taken to Asia, where these two species became hybridized. Today, in tropical and semitropical regions, they are grown in their original forms, as well as all imaginable hybrid combinations with fluted and crinkled petals.

However, we need not sigh for such colorful plants in our northern gardens. We have three or four species native in eastern North America whose modern garden forms possibly even surpass their tropical relatives in showiness. Why these hardy and brilliantly colored American forms of *Hibiscus* (called Rosemallow in the trade) are not more often grown is a puzzle.

The other flower peeping into our picture is the Yellow Hibiscus, *H. manihot*. This can be grown from seed and handled as an annual in our gardens; with proper care some will produce flowers six to nine inches in diameter. One of its short pods is shown on the opposite page. In the Old World Tropics a very similar plant but with smaller flowers and much longer pods has long been cultivated for food.

The links between certain related ornamental and food plants are obscure, for their derivations took place thousands of years ago. But in my opinion both of these plants were derived from a formerly wide-ranging species which the early peoples from southeastern Asia to Africa once cultivated. From this plant variant strains were selected, some for their flowers and others for their pods. This large podded type, now classified as *Hibiscus esculentus*, and today common throughout the Tropics, was introduced to America from Africa along with its names okra and gumbo.

Long Ago Men Grew These Gorgeous Plants as Food in Tropical East Asia. Hibiscus, or Rose-of-China (left), still lends its buds to curries. The East Indian Lotus (center) calls to mind the Lotus-eaters, though they did not consume this form. Yellow Hibiscus (upper right) has a popular vegetable relative, okra.

73

Chinese Mountainsides Yield Treasures

SOME YEARS AGO in tracing plant origins I had translated parts of a volume by Sheng-Nung, an estimable Chinese gentleman who lived more than 4,600 years ago. What impressed me was not that the Chinese cultivated plants so early, for theirs is an ancient civilization, but that they had already selected and named so many varieties. This meant they had been cultivating these plants many centuries earlier.

We know little of ornamental gardening in early China, but when the Venetian, Marco Polo, journeyed there between A. D. 1272 and 1293 and visited the court of Kublai Khan at Xanadu, he was amazed at the splendor and plant wealth of the gardens. For centuries many of these plants had wandered down old trade routes to Persia, and from there to Europe. Even so, Europeans of Marco Polo's day refused to believe what he had seen in Chinese gardens.

No civilization of any stature has yet arisen which has not developed some ornamental gardens, but the ancient Chinese gardeners were especially fortunate; perhaps nowhere in the Temperate Zones is there a region richer in potential materials. Also, vast China has many soil types and climates, each with its own set of species. And that is all in our favor, for from them we may choose those which fit almost every type of climate and soil we have.

REGAL LILY (*Lilium regale*): Let us first "consider the lilies of the field; they toil not. . . ." But how we ourselves toil to perfect them in our gardens! Its nearly 100 wild species leave scarcely a region in the Northern Hemisphere without the genus *Lilium*. So striking is this plant that everywhere it grew wild it was brought into gardens. To represent China, one might easily choose the old Tiger Lily (*L. tigrinum*), which, with its tawny-red flowers splotched with purple black, is perhaps the most widely grown species. Or we might choose— but why go down the list of Chinese species? Let us just take the Regal Lily, thought by many to be the Queen of the genus.

Still, have you ever seen Humboldt's Lily growing wild in the Sierra Nevada, or the towering *Lilium superbum*—I've seen it with 40 flowers on a single plant—in the spruce-rimmed glades of our southern Appalachians? But the Sierras and the Great Smokies are not in China.

ABELIA (*Abelia grandiflora*): For a shrubby member of the Honeysuckle family from China we might have chosen any one of several excellent flowering Honeysuckles. Also, there is the increasingly popular *Viburnum carlesi*, with its fragrant white blooms; but actually it is Korean. And what about the showy "Weigelas"? Botanically, they are Diervillas, and *D. florida* from North China has brought hardiness and a deep rose color to our modern hybrids. But the Weigelas bloom early and fade soon.

For our painting we have chosen *Abelia grandiflora*, a garden hybrid which has the most desirable qualities of its wild parents. Not too choosy about soils, partly evergreen, usually compact and graceful, it flowers nearly constantly from June until heavy frost. It is the work-horse of the shrubby border, particularly during the vegetative doldrums of late summer. The genus was named for Clarke Abel (1780–1826), physician and author, who lived in China.

PEONY (*Paeonia*, various species): The Chinese have been cultivating their favorite, the Peony, for thousands of years. Writings of more than 800 years ago record large collections; one enthusiast had 60,000 plants in his garden. Originally with five or perhaps ten petals, the double-flowered forms resulted from progressive sterilization of the stamens, accompanied by enlargement of the filaments into colored petal-like structures. Two main types are grown: common herbaceous peonies and "tree" peonies (actually shrubby plants seldom over five feet tall). With recent hybrid combinations, we now can look forward to a whole new series of forms.

China's Ancient Gardens Sent Us These Beauties. Plants like these astonished Marco Polo on his 13th-century journeys. Regal Lily crowns the painting. Peony (below) displays a double-flowered garden form. Hard-working Abelia (right), a shrubby member of the Honeysuckle family, blooms until heavy frost.

More Plants from Age-old China

AN OLD CHINESE STORY, dealing with wanderlust, tells us that he who lives beside a waterfall need not travel to listen to the ocean, for water sounds much the same whether dashing against a rocky shore or pouring over stones. The legend ends: "Furthermore, when you are away, who will tend your garden?"

CAMELLIA: Although introduced into Western gardens mainly by way of Japan and therefore known under such historically misleading names as *Camellia japonica* and *C. sasanqua* (the latter derived from a Japanese vernacular name), our garden Camellias can be traced back to forms once wild in China. Botanically, China's Tea Plant is a close relative.

HOLLYHOCK (*Althaea rosea*): Rearing its showy spikes of flowers in our midsummer gardens, this species now comes in so many shades and forms that our grandmothers scarcely would recognize this old favorite.

CHINA ASTER (*Callistephus chinensis*): In its wild form this species has a single series of petal-like, purplish-blue ray flowers around the margin and a large number of small yellow flowers in the center of the head. Cultivated double forms are now generally seen. Selected types vary greatly in color, but no really yellow forms are known. *Callistephus* is the Greek for "beautiful crown" and *chinensis* means "living in, or from China." Hence this plant might well be called "The Chinese Beautiful-Crown."

BLACKBERRY-LILY (*Belamcanda chinensis*): This plant once almost disappeared from gardens, but thanks to a newer series of color forms and larger, more showy flowers, it promises to be popular again. Its common name is

derived from the blackberrylike appearance of the ripe fruit after it splits open, exposing the black seed. However, the plant is neither a blackberry nor a lily—it is a member of the Iris family. Why not call this pretty flower by its real name? After all, it is only a slightly modified form of the one it has carried for untold centuries in its native home. Slowly repeat the syllables Bel-am-CAN-da until the natural music they make becomes familiar.

CHRYSANTHEMUM: Back against the wall in our picture is a bed of Chrysanthemums, one of the countless forms in which this great group of showy plants occurs. For convenience, botanists have classified the garden and florists' "mums" as a single species, *Chrysanthemum morifolium*, but they have been grown and hybridized for so many centuries there seems little chance of determining exactly from which wild species they have come. All we know is that, primarily, our modern garden mums are of Chinese origin.

CLEMATIS (*Clematis lanuginosa*): Scrambling over the wall is a plant of the largest flowered of all known wild species of this remarkable genus. Combined with brighter-colored species, such as the southwestern Asiatic and southern European *C. viticella* and the Japanese *C. patens*, this Chinese species is the most important parent of our many large-flowered, hybrid garden forms, such as the popular Jackman's Clematis. Frost-free gardens have their own special kinds.

FORSYTHIA: Here the scientific name, *Forsythia*, actually is more often used than the so-called common name, Golden Bells. Two species are grown, *Forsythia viridissima*, and the somewhat pendulous-branched *F. suspensa*, as well as their hybrid, *F. intermedia*. How did this early, spring-flowering Forsythia get into a picture with mainly late summer bloomers? Actually, we chased him away several times. But he sneaked back persistently and peered through the Moon Gate, almost as if hissing in old sibilant Mandarinese: "You don't *dare* leave me out of this! I'm Chinese too!"

From China Come These Bright Plants Now So Familiar to the West. Variegated Camellias straddle the old-fashioned Hollyhock (top). At lower left is China Aster; at lower right, Blackberry Lily. Clematis grows on the wall, Chrysanthemum at its base. Forsythia peers through the moon gate.

Patient Gardeners of Old Japan

THE JAPANESE ISLANDS cover about the same range of latitude one finds from New England to Florida. Toward the south where winters were mild the Japanese had a calendar marked by a continuous succession of flowers.

This floral calendar was so arranged that New Year's Day fell in our February, just as the first Plum blossoms opened. These were followed in March by the Peach and Cherry. May brought the *fuji*, or Wisteria. June was made beautiful with Irises and Peonies. In July came the East Indian Lotus.

The late summer—August and September— was marked by various kinds of Hibiscus, with autumn heralded by the October Chrysanthemums. And the winter months, closing out the Japanese year, were the time when the Tea Plant and various Camellias bloomed.

Patient old Japanese gardeners with their keen eyes for selection gave to the world many choice ornamental varieties. Because they also made free use of non-native species, Japan is the door through which many Chinese and other Asiatic plants came to us.

JAPANESE WISTERIA (*Wisteria floribunda*): This strikingly beautiful member of the Pea family has long been a favorite and in the hands of Japanese selectors has yielded numerous garden forms. In its original state the flowers apparently were purplish and in clusters (called racemes) less than a foot long. By careful selection the basic colors have been separated, intensified, or diluted to pastel shades, and recombined by hybridization so that tints range from deep violet to light blue, rose, pink, and white.

Other selections yielded plants with racemes up to three or four feet long; this group, designated variety *macrobotrys*, also has many races varying in color, size, and shape of their flowers.

Long Ago Japan Domesticated Its Own Wild Flowers and Improved Its Neighbors'. Japanese Wisteria frames the snow-capped volcano. Bleeding Heart is at lower center and Japanese Iris at right. Dwarfed Pine and Flowering Cherry stand in pots. Japanese Azaleas grow near the stone lantern in the distance.

Several Chinese species also are grown, such as *W. sinensis*, with its flowers either blue-violet or white, and *W. venusta*, with its large white flowers on short racemes. Native American Wisterias, as *W. frutescens* of our own Southeast and *W. macrostachya* of our South Central States, are sometimes cultivated. The genus name honors Caspar Wistar (1761–1818), University of Pennsylvania anatomy professor, but was spelled with an "e"—*Wisteria*—by its original namer, probably for reasons of euphony.

BLEEDING HEART (*Dicentra spectabilis*): This Japanese member of the Fumitory family, most spectacular of its genus, has long been popular in American gardens. Like many North Temperate genera, *Dicentra* has wild species both in Asia and in North America. The two American species are *D. formosa* of the Pacific coast mountains and *D. eximia* of the southern Appalachians. Another American member of this family, *Adlumia fungosa*, is known in various regions as Allegheny-Vine, Climbing Fumitory, or Mountain Fringe.

JAPANESE IRIS (*Iris kaempferi* and *I. laevigata*): In the wild, *Iris kaempferi* is said to have reddish-purple flowers and *I. laevigata* blue ones. Although usually sold under the name of *Iris kaempferi*, apparently both species (and probably others) are involved in the present races of this group. The Japanese have hundreds of named varieties; in recent years our own Iris breeders have added many more.

AZALEA (*Rhododendron*, various species): Botanically speaking, the Azaleas belong in the genus *Rhododendron*. The so-called "Japanese" Azaleas, for the most part, are the result of hybridization between native Japanese species and some introduced there long ago from China.

In our picture two artificially dwarfed trees also are shown. One is the pine. Several species were used, but the Japanese Red Pine seems to have been a favorite. The other is the Flowering Cherry. Japanese gardeners also made use of the Flowering Almond and the Peach, both native in China, to produce dwarfed flowering trees.

79

Australian Plants and Geography

WE WHO STUDY the natural distribution of plants are intrigued by those of Australia. Many have close connections elsewhere, for example in Africa, and by way of Tasmania and New Zealand, in southern South America. These relationships are so close that we are forced to conclude that at one time Australia was in some way connected by land with these faraway areas.

Later, Australia became isolated from the rest of the world—long enough to develop its own peculiar plant and animal species. This last great inhabited continent to be discovered has provided many excellent items for today's gardens.

In 1768 Sir Joseph Banks and his associate Daniel Solander (southern gardeners remember him in the genus *Solandra*) sailed with Captain Cook on the first of his memorable voyages. From the region about a certain bay in Australia they collected hundreds of different species of plants; to commemorate this great haul, the place was named Botany Bay.

EUCALYPTUS or GUM TREE (*Eucalyptus*, various species): The approximately 300 species of Eucalyptus are mainly Australian, although they have been widely planted elsewhere in tropical and subtropical regions. Some grow rapidly, yielding firewood and lumber in a comparatively few years. In deforested parts of South America Eucalyptus has been introduced and is almost the only tree seen for miles. About a dozen species, including the Blue Gum (*E. globulus*), are regularly grown in California and to some extent in Florida. In its home in Australia the Blue Gum may reach a height of 300 feet.

Other species are lower growing and often strikingly ornamental, with bright scarlet or pink flowers (e.g., *E. ficifolia*), or curiously shaped, grayish-silvery leaves (e.g., *E. polyanthemos*). Because of the unusual shapes and colors of the leaves, young shoots of various species are now often seen in florists' shops.

The Eucalyptus belongs to the Myrtle family. This large family of plants, with about 75 genera and 3,000 species, has many members; the true Myrtle of the Classical Period, native around the Mediterranean, is only one. Many tropical or subtropical gardens contain such interesting

fruit trees of the Myrtle family as the South American pitanga or Surinam cherry, the Malayan rose apple, the Australian brush cherry, the East Indian jambolan plum, and the tropical American guava.

Cloves are the flower buds of one of this family native in the Moluccas; allspice is the dried, unripe berry of another from the West Indies and Central America. Bay rum is distilled from the leaves of still another native in the Caribbean and northern South America.

BOTTLE-BRUSH (*Callistemon rigidus*): This also is a member of the Myrtle family. There are about 25 species of this showy Australian genus of shrubby trees. The closely related Australian Cajuput tree or Punk tree (*Melaleuca leucadendron*), with its dense clusters of creamy white flowers, is often planted in Florida, where it has escaped and in places become weedy.

STRAWFLOWER (*Helichrysum bracteatum*): These are so common that we are inclined to forget their native home is Australia. Cut at the proper stage as they open, and hung upside-down to dry, they make excellent "everlasting" winter bouquets. The name *Helichrysum* is an apt compound of two words meaning sun-gold.

SWAN RIVER DAISY (*Brachycome iberidifolia*): Named for its native region in Australia, this pretty and easily grown annual is worthy of a place in any garden.

BLUE LACE-FLOWER (*Trachymene coerulea*): Sometimes erroneously listed in seed catalogues as "Didiscus coerulea," this delicate Australian is often grown as a garden decorative. It is related to the European Queen-Anne's-Lace (*Daucus carota*), now a weed in our lots and fields.

Australia, Last-discovered Inhabited Continent, Gave the World Many Unusual Plants. Bottle-Brush hangs above Strawflowers and Swan River Daisies nod below at left. Right: Blue Lace-Flower adds a delicate note. Eucalyptus (background), prized for its rapid growth and ornamental foliage, has been brought to the Americas.

South America Rich in Plant Life

PLACE CALIFORNIA'S COAST on the Pacific shore of Peru and only the tips of Maine and Florida would project into the Atlantic on the opposite side of South America. The Amazon basin alone is two thirds as large as the continental United States; it is rarely more than a few hundred feet above sea level, yet its western boundary is marked by one of the highest continuous mountain ranges in the world. Almost nowhere in some 4,000 miles is there a pass lower than 10,000 feet.

Such is the magnificent scale upon which South America is built. Snow-capped mountains rise out of equatorial jungles. Parts of the eastern slopes of the Andes are among the world's wettest regions, while segments of the narrow coastal strip, a few miles away on the western side of this range, are among the driest.

The continent's abundant plant life matches its geographical and climatic diversity. Many of these plants have been brought into our gardens. Most, in native haunts, are perennials. Some, like the Fuchsia opposite, are best grown from cuttings; others shown, although still potential perennials, bloom soon enough from seed to be grown as annuals in the north.

FUCHSIA (*Fuchsia*, various species): The numerous species of this member of the Evening-Primrose family are mostly shrubby. Primarily South American, a few venture naturally as far north as Mexico; three or four species are found in New Zealand. Some forms in the Andes have delicate little bell-like crimson flowers less than an inch long, but I have seen plants ten feet high covered with masses of salmony-red flowers up to four or five inches long. The one shown is a form of *Fuchsia magellanica*, originally native from Peru southward to the bleak hills of Tierra del Fuego; certain varieties, with some protection, are reasonably hardy outdoors at least as far north as New York.

Closely related but frost-sensitive forms occur northward through Central America. Most decorative Fuchsias we see are hybrids, probably between forms of *F. magellanica* and the showier Mexican *F. fulgens*. The genus name honors Leonhard Fuchs, eminent 16th century botanist.

PETUNIA (*Petunia hybrida*): As the name implies, our garden Petunias are hybrids, the parent species being the white *P. axillaris* and the purplish-violet *P. violacea*, both originally from Argentina. A sorting out of the basic colors which, in combination, gave the purplish tint to the wild *P. violacea* has produced today's bluish and rosy-pink forms; the white forms hark back to the *P. axillaris* ancestor.

CUP-FLOWER (*Nierembergia*, several species): Two species are widely grown, the dainty Brazilian *N. gracilis* and the more robust Chilean *N. frutescens*, the latter often as a shrubby pot plant. The genus was named for John Eusebius Nieremberg, first professor of natural history at the University of Madrid. The Nierembergias and Petunias belong to the same plant family as the potato, tomato, and tobacco. Other South American members of this same family are Salpiglossis, Schizanthus, Browallia, and the sometimes foot-long Angels Trumpet.

GARDEN VERBENA (*Verbena hortensis*): The garden forms of this group are not referable to any one wild species. One of the principal parents seems to have been a scarlet-flowered species wild in Argentina and southern Brazil, but now hybridized with a purplish-flowered species from southern Brazil and Paraguay and a whitish-flowered species widespread in parts of southern South America. The result is the present wide range of colors in the modern Garden Verbena.

SCARLET SAGE (*Salvia splendens*): In its native haunts in Brazil this common garden plant is a shrubby perennial with scarlet flowers. Quick-blooming forms with flower color also in adjacent plant parts are now available, varying from the scarlet to crimson, purple, even white.

Some Old Garden Favorites Trace Their Ancestry to South America's Plains and Andes. Fuchsia (top), whose galaxy of Andean forms ever amazes the collector, now has many garden varieties. Its delicate bells almost touch Garden Verbena. Left: Petunias rear their heads. Cup-Flowers (left) and Scarlet Sage occupy the corners

From South American Jungles

JUNGLE PLANTS in our northern gardens? One would think our climate unsuitable for them. The plant explorer sometimes has difficulty convincing people that our sweltering northern summers may be quite as tropical as the climate he finds in much of the South American jungle. But the proof lies in our many common plants, especially among the annuals, which come from there, as—alas!—do some pestiferous weeds which vie for space along our garden paths.

SPIDER FLOWER (*Cleome spinosa*): This increasingly popular garden plant is a member of the Caper family; its common name is derived from the spidery appearance of its wide-spreading stamens. Spider Flowers usually come in light, rosy-purple shades, but white and pink forms are now fairly common. The pungent foliage suggests just a little of the primal and earthy odors so characteristic of its jungle home.

MORNING GLORY (*Ipomoea*, various species): There are, around the world, about 400 species of wild Morning Glories, a large number of them native in the American Tropics. In their native haunts many of these are rampant weeds. All of the true Morning Glories belong to the genus *Ipomoea*; in color they range from red (which is rare) through purple and blue to white, with occasional mottled and striped forms. Many wild species have been cultivated and used by hybridists to produce some of our modern garden types. The two most often grown are *Ipomoea purpurea*, usually seen in purplish-blue shades, and the light blue garden form of *I. tricolor*.

Few of us recognize as a Morning Glory one we grow in our vegetable gardens: *I. batatas*, the common sweet potato. It rarely flowers in the north, but in its jungle home the pretty blue blossoms on trailing vines are unmistakable.

South America's Jungle Denizens Enjoy Our Hot and Humid Northern Summers. Morning Glory (left) looks up at tall and pungent Spider Flower. Double-flowered Nasturtiums hug its base. Cypress Vine weaves a lacework pattern to the right. Victoria Waterlilies float six-foot rafts in the stream; Cannas border the forest.

CYPRESS VINE (*Quamoclit pennata*): This dainty scarlet-flowered, finely cut-leafed climber has long been a garden favorite, but it is now somewhat less common than the Cardinal Climber. The latter is a hybrid between the species shown here and another with coarse and undivided leaves, *Quamoclit coccinea*. We find both parent species in our southern States, probably as escapes from gardens. The Quamoclits are close relatives of the Morning Glories.

NASTURTIUM (*Tropaeolum majus*): Fifty-odd species of wild Nasturtiums range throughout tropical America from southern Mexico to Chile. Some have been hybridized, usually just enough to bring in the red and orangey colors. Their rapid growth and early, free-flowering habit—so necessary in our northern gardens—have been obtained primarily from the wild, yellow-flowered *Tropaeolum majus* ancestor. Double-flowered forms are now obtainable in various colors.

VICTORIA WATERLILY: Although generally sold under the botanical name of *Victoria regia*, the plant usually turns out to be another species, *Victoria cruziana*; both are South American. This tropical waterlily is grown more for its enormous leaves—up to six feet across—with their curiously up-turned margins than for its flowers. Admittedly not for tub culture, this lily, given ample space, will provide quite a show.

CANNA: Growing along streams or at the edge of the forest, wild Cannas—of which there are quite a few species, some with red and some with yellow flowers—are a characteristic part of the American jungle scene. The old Indian Shot (*Canna indica*, not from India but actually an American species), with its bright-red but small flowers and coarse "leggy" growth, is giving way in our gardens to the newer, compact, large-flowered hybrid forms. The floppy flowered *Canna flaccida* of the Florida Everglades and Georgia's coastal swamps, together with other more tropical American species, has contributed much to the modern "orchid-flowered" hybrid garden Cannas. The large parts of the Canna flower which look like petals are sterile stamens.

Mexican Love of Flowers

NOT SO LONG ago I climbed to the top of the huge pyramid shown opposite and looked out across that great mountain-rimmed plain on which are strewn the relics of what certainly was a most remarkable civilization.

Standing there, I could but wonder how Teotihuacán's temples and palaces really looked when peopled by their proud builders. Did they stand there resplendent, but bare, beneath a burnished sun? Probably not. We know that the ancient Mexicans had extensive gardens before the coming of the Conquistadores, for Cortés found true botanical gardens and stood in awe before their floral splendors.

It is no accident that today one finds the Mexican *patio* filled with potted plants or hanging baskets of ferns, trailing vines, or succulents. And it is a mean hut indeed which has no cherished plant, even if grown in nothing more than an old tin can. I have watched Mexican gardeners deftly tend their plants, with an understanding that could stem only from centuries of garden lore passed from father to son.

And so I should like to think that those warriors of old lined their wide avenues with trees and planted their temple and palace grounds to pleasant shrubs and flowering herbs. It must have been so; otherwise the love of green growing things would not have persisted so strongly in their descendants. Gone now are the crested warriors, the ancient priests and kings; gone are their terraced gardens, all turned to dust and rubble.

Out of this ancient way of life the only thing that really lasted was the love of beauty and of flowers, cherished through all the bitter years in the hearts of the Mexican people. There surely must be a moral here, but I am not philosopher enough to point it out and so can only light my pipe and go about my business.

Mexico Offers Flowers of the Aztecs. Before Cortés, Mexican gardeners selected double Dahlias; two forms are shown at top, above a wild single type. Gaudy Tiger-Flowers, sacred to the jaguar cult, stand on right. Behind, Pyramid of the Sun rises amid a deserted city the Aztecs named Teotihuacán, "place where the gods reside."

DAHLIA: Unlike so many plants, the first Dahlia introduced into European gardens was not of the wild or "single" type; already the old Aztec gardeners had so hybridized and selected it that, even today, we are undecided which of the wild species were its ancestors. Hybridists have since made available a wide variety of forms, and it can be truly said that the Dahlia is king of our late summer gardens.

Grown in large quantity, the tubers sometimes present a winter-storage problem if one is not properly equipped. However, certain types of Dahlia can be grown from seed each year. Seed sown in a sunny window in late February or in March will produce plants for setting out at the usual time; if pinched back several times to make them branch, these will grow into quite sizable bushes by midsummer and produce a wealth of bloom.

The flowers probably will not be of the massive "double decorative" type but will abound in interesting shades and forms, usually of the single or semiwild type. If some seedling plant proves particularly interesting, its tubers can be lifted and stored for planting the next year.

The genus name honors Andreas Dahl, a Swedish botanist and pupil of the great Linnaeus. Decorative as they are, Dahlias were first used by ancient Mexicans as food. The tubers contain a healthful starchy substance, inulin.

TIGER-FLOWER (*Tigridia pavonia*): Gaudily spotted, the Tiger-Flower must have been common in Aztec gardens, for it was sacred to the jaguar (*tigre*) cult. The lower of the two examples shown is nearest the wild type in color; garden forms now also come in varying shades and patterns of lilac, yellow, and even white.

It is a mystery to me why this striking member of the Iris family is not more often seen in our gardens, for it is not difficult to grow. Any gardener, even with limited space, can make his own hybrids and select those color forms he likes best. Grown from seed, Tigridia plants flower freely about the third year. The corms are lifted in the autumn and stored; in fact, Tigridia culture is so similar to that of the Gladiolus that it should cause no trouble at all.

Mexico, Happy Hunting Ground for Botanists

AMID THE FLORAL SPLENDORS on the opposite page our artist has shown the typical home of a Zapotec Indian surrounded by its living cactus fence. This is not just any house; it is in the State of Oaxaca in southern Mexico in the village of Mitla. It was from Mitla that my Zapotec friend and companion Goopar and I set out for the great mountain called Zempoaltepec; it was to Mitla and his home that we returned weeks later, our pack mules laden with pressed specimens, living plants, and seeds (page 46).

COSMOS: The genus *Cosmos*, with about 20 species, is entirely tropical American. The two species most frequently grown in our gardens are both Mexican. The more common of these is *Cosmos bipinnatus*, well known in its various crimson, pink, and white forms. The other species is *Cosmos sulphureus*, yellow-flowered as its specific name would indicate. Today apparent hybrid garden forms exist, but the true *C. sulphureus* is easily recognized by longer central (disc) flowers with their dark colored stamens sticking out farther than those of *C. bipinnatus*.

Cosmos are not suited for low bedding purposes, and anybody who tries to treat them thus robs himself of a magnificent show. I would start mine early, growing them in well enriched soil so that by late summer the plants would be wide-branched and not less than six feet tall. Sometimes they can be forced to as high as ten feet with as many as a hundred blooms at once.

ZINNIA (*Zinnia elegans*): The wild material of this well-known garden plant has rather uninteresting dull-purplish blooms; in this form they were first introduced into European and American gardens. What has happened since is a living monument to the science—also the art—of the hybridist and selector for, as Dr. L. H. Bailey, for many years Nestor of American horticulture, once remarked, they now are "of nearly every color except blue and green."

I strongly suspect that another Mexican species, *Zinnia haageana*, through hybridization, has contributed something in the way of red and orange to the color forms of *elegans*. This latter species, usually more dwarf and with smaller blooms than *elegans*, is also offered by many seedsmen in various colors and shapes.

Like the Cosmos, Dahlia, Daisy, and various others in this series, the Zinnia belongs to the Sunflower family, or Compositae. If one examines the flower of a Zinnia carefully, it will be noted that actually it is not a single flower. In the wild, or single, forms there generally are two types of flowers present, the inner or "disc" flowers and the outer, highly modified and petal-like "ray" flowers. In the Zinnia, as in other members of this family, the so-called double forms are merely those in which the disc flowers have taken on the characteristics of the ray flowers. This may readily be seen by examining one of the "half-double" types.

Various garden Zinnias are shown opposite. Sometimes in an unnamed mixture a plant will appear with flowers like the one farthest right. Such throwbacks approach the wild type.

POINSETTIA (*Euphorbia pulcherrima*): In our high school Latin class probably one of the first adjectives we learned was *pulcher*, meaning beautiful or handsome. Later we also learned that the Romans had intensifiers which they tacked on to their adjectives. Thus when the old botanist Karl Ludwig Willdenow was searching for a suitable name for his new species of Euphorbia about 150 years ago—and scientific botanical names are in Latin, or a Latinized form of Greek—he scarcely could avoid calling it "the *very* beautiful Euphorbia," or *Euphorbia pulcherrima*.

As in Madagascar's Crown-of-Thorns (page 71), a related species, the bright scarlet objects which make the Poinsettia of Mexico so handsome actually are not parts of the flowers but highly modified petal-like leaves called bracts.

Living Cactus Fence in Oaxaca, Mexico, Guards a Zapotec Indian's Home. Several species of Cosmos sway across the top. Below them grow Zinnias of modern garden form; a wild type stems out to right. The handsome scarlet bracts of the Poinsettia of Mexico brighten the lower right corner.

More Native Mexicans

HERE ARE MORE native Mexicans and an indication of how they got their common names.

FRANGIPANI (*Plumeria rubra*): In attempting to trace the origin of the name Frangipani, we find that it was applied to a French pastry named for its inventor, the Marquis Frangipani, a French general. But Frangipani (or Frangipanni) is not a French name; it is basically Italian and goes back to an old Roman family first prominent during the Middle Ages. As another clue, there was an old perfume called Frangipani distilled from a red jasmine. Then in another work we discovered that our plant once was called Tree Jasmine. Here is the link. Now to fit the facts together.

The fragrant red jasmines most likely to have been used in perfumes seem to be Asiatic. But might they not have been brought to Rome from Asia during the days of the Empire? From old writings we know there was keen rivalry among the Romans for the acquisition of these exotics. If such a remarkable plant were being grown by a particular family, what would be more natural than for their friends to ask: "Have you seen the new plant which the Frangipanni's have blooming in their garden? Such red flowers! And so fragrant!"

Lacking a local name, it would become "Frangipanni's plant," later to be shortened to Frangipani. This is not unusual. Forsythia honors an English horticulturist, William Forsythe, and Wisteria (with a slight change of spelling) commemorates Caspar Wistar of Philadelphia.

How the name Frangipani became transferred from the perfume-yielding red jasmine to the sweet scented, reddish-flowered tree shown opposite probably never will be known, but there are literally hundreds of such name-transfers. Take the Marigold. There is only one true Marigold, the Pot Marigold of Europe (page 51); yet the yellow and orangey Mexican flowers on the opposite page also are called Marigolds. And we must not forget that there was a time when *our* Frangipani was called Tree Jasmine.

The species shown here is native in Mexico; it occurs wild also in Central America and northern South America. It is commonly planted in tropical regions and often has escaped, especially in the West Indies. Other tropical American species of *Plumeria* have white or yellow flowers (again, one of them is Mexican). These also are often planted, and hybrids are grown.

FRENCH AND AFRICAN MARIGOLDS (*Tagetes*, several species): The trail of the French and African Marigolds is a bit clearer. The genus *Tagetes* is entirely American, its 20 or so species ranging from New Mexico and Arizona southward into Argentina. Those which immediately concern us are native in Mexico, and probably were grown in the old pre-Conquest gardens. They found their way into the early Spanish-American gardens and soon were sent to Spain, whence they were carried to monastery gardens in Africa and France.

By the time these plants reached northern European gardens all knowledge of their real origin had been lost. Being yellowish orange, in England they were called marigolds (from Mary's Gold); but to differentiate them from the native European Marigold (now called Pot Marigold) they became French Marigolds and African Marigolds; these names then came to us from England.

Several modern garden forms of the taller "African" Marigold (*Tagetes erecta*) with its larger flower heads and the smaller, usually reddish-suffused "French" Marigold (*T. patula*) are shown here as well as a few wild species.

I once was in a Mexican store as a shipment of seed from the States was being unpacked. Two of the gaily-colored packets, the proprietor proudly assured me, were "new in Mexico." I smiled inwardly, for I had seen them wild in the hills. After centuries of travel and two Atlantic crossings, the "African" and "French" Marigolds had come home.

Mexico's Floral Album Contains Exotic Names; Our Genealogist Clears Their Titles. At top is Frangipani, whose name originally was applied to an Asiatic jasmine. Left: large "African" Marigolds and (below and center) single and double "French" Marigolds, all native Mexicans. At the right margin: wild Marigolds.

Garden Beauties from America's West

NORTH AMERICA is rich in potential ornamentals. But ours is a comparatively new country and its culture came ready-made. The early settlers faced an unknown wilderness. In clearings made for crops, any shoot which sprang up was a weed to be destroyed. But as the settlements grew and life became secure, flower gardens were planted.

Because of strong cultural ties the first flowers raised were mostly European. The plant explorers who followed realized the potentialities of our native species and sent large numbers of them to Europe. Many eastern seaboard plants have since returned, quite different in form and in many beautiful varieties.

The plants of western North America appeared in gardens only about a century ago, most of them even more recently. Rarely do we see them in anything other than their original wild forms. Since they are less adaptable and demand conditions similar to those in nature, western wild flowers are difficult subjects for general gardening. These plants, especially those from the Pacific Northwest, are more often grown in England, where the climate is similar, than in southern, midwestern, or eastern gardens.

Anyone who has ridden the trails between the Great Plains and the Pacific will realize how regrettable it is that only a few of these worthy species may be classed as common and widespread garden flowers. How some of the Bitter-roots (*Lewisia*) resent being moved! Acres of Avalanche Lilies (*Erythronium montanum*) in the Cascades sometimes push through the last three inches of snow to bloom on schedule, only to dwindle to nothing a few years after being planted in a garden. Hosts of yellow-, orange-, pink-, and white-tufted Eriogonums grow naturally under seemingly impossible conditions; yet relatively few do well in our gardens, even with the best care and attention. And most of the Mariposas or Butterfly-Tulips (*Calochortus*) spurn permanent sanctuary in civilization.

These and a hundred other flowers ought to be widespread in gardens but usually tolerate domestication only under special conditions. But let us be patient; many will yet be broken of their wild habits. Most of the newer blue garden Columbines descended from the wild *Aquilegia coerulea* of the Rocky Mountains, and others show equal promise. Here are a few Westerners already common in our gardens.

CLARKIA (*Clarkia elegans*): This fine annual, native in California, comes in several shades, also in frilly double forms. The generic name honors William Clark, associate of Meriwether Lewis (for whom *Lewisia* was named), both sent by Thomas Jefferson to explore to the Pacific.

CALIFORNIA POPPY (*Eschscholtzia californica*): Originally yellow or orangey, this popular garden plant, named for J. F. Eschscholtz, a botanist on Kotzebue's Russian expedition into the Pacific, 1823–1826, now displays other colors.

BLANKET-FLOWER (*Gaillardia pulchella*): When this gaudy plant is seen in masses in its native haunts, the origin of its common name becomes obvious. Native from the Ozarks south to the Gulf and west across the Great Plains to Arizona, it is now more widely established. Introduced into Europe from Louisiana in early colonial days, it was named in honor of Gaillard de Marentonneau, French patron of botany.

LUPINE (*Lupinus*, various species): Except for a relatively few kinds in Europe, Asia Minor and Africa, the 300 species of Lupine are all native in the Western Hemisphere. Capable of making great, carpetlike displays, the wild species often are introduced into gardens. Some have been hybridized. Our more common perennial garden forms seem to stem primarily from West Coast species, whereas the more showy annuals derive from species wild in Mexico, Central, and Andean South America.

Many Flowers of Western States Refuse to Be Tamed; These Tolerate Gardeners. Lupines, thick as Texas Bluebonnets, cover the hillside. Center: Blanket-Flowers stand below California Poppies. Clarkia (left) is one of the namesakes of the Lewis and Clark Expedition. The floral riches of the West have only begun to be tapped.

Wild Flower, or Garden Plant?

IT IS SOMETIMES difficult to distinguish a wild flower from a weed. But when either is brought into a garden it ceases to be wild and becomes a horticultural object. To the farmer in eastern North America, the plants opposite may sometimes be weeds; to the field naturalist they are wild flowers; to the gardener they are cherished subjects in the perennial border, especially when, in the skilled hands of the hybridist and selector, they yield unusual garden forms.

OSWEGO TEA (*Monarda didyma*): During the development of their civilizations the ancient peoples around the Mediterranean experimented with their native plants. They discovered among the region's condiments and medicinal herbs such useful things as Rosemary, Common Sage, Clary, Lavender, Woundwort, Thyme, Pennyroyal, Horehound, Lemon Balm, Marjoram, Hyssop, and both Summer Savory and Winter Savory—all members of the Mint family.

When the cultivation of useful plants spread to Europe from the Mediterranean, these plants became standard in cottage, monastery, and castle gardens. Colonists brought them to America. But always in this new country there were pioneers pushing on ahead of established gardens who were forced to seek native substitutes. America did not fail them.

Two useful plants they found were of this same Mint family, Oswego Tea (*Monarda didyma*) and Wild Bergamot (*Monarda fistulosa*). Both became fixtures in early American herb gardens along with imported relatives. Later, when herb gardens went out of style (they are again becoming popular), they moved to the flower garden. For a time pale purplish-flowered Wild Bergamot—similar to but less striking than originally reddish-scarlet Oswego Tea—almost went into eclipse, but it is making a strong comeback in perennial borders. Both now have variously colored garden forms.

SUMMER PERENNIAL PHLOX (*Phlox paniculata*): Although variations do occur in the wild, most plants of this species growing naturally have pinkish-purple flowers. From these, salmon, rose, magenta, purple, scarlet, buff, and white garden forms have been developed. Among the more popular of the 10 or 12 other native North American species of this genus introduced into gardens are the highly variable, spring-flowering Moss-Pink (*Phlox subulata*), much used in rockeries, and the even more variable, low-growing Texas annual, *Phlox drummondi*. European and American hybridists have produced many forms in this group.

MICHAELMAS DAISIES (*Aster*, various species): Named for St. Michael, whose festival, Michael's Mass, is celebrated September 29, when certain forms are at the height of bloom, this splendid group of perennials now has great favor with gardeners. I admit they put on a great show in the autumn, but still suspect that part of their popularity lies in their name and in the common supposition that they come from a foreign land. Actually, they are as American as pumpkin pie or corn-on-the-cob.

The plant explorers who came to America about two centuries ago seized upon these plants and took them back to Europe, where they became a garden sensation. When the art of hybridizing became well known, these plants were used and many new and intermediate forms were developed. Yet American farmers were still mowing them down to clear their fence rows and pastures, and most American gardeners considered them only roadside weeds. The few who cultivated our native Asters finally were vindicated when the plants became popular.

One species which stands out in this group is the New England Aster (*Aster novae-angliae*) whose flower heads, once deep purple, are now split into blue, pink, reddish, and white forms. A distinguished group of plants with small or intermediate-sized, often white flower heads has resulted from hybridization with other species.

Easterners Did Not Appreciate American "Weeds" Until Europe Made Them Fashionable. Native Asters (lower left) made a sensation abroad and came home to America with name changed to Michaelmas Daisies. Oswego Tea (right) moved from pioneers' herb plots into flower gardens. Summer Perennial Phlox crowns painting.

Gems from the Southeastern United States

RICH AS IS THE FLORAL LIFE of our southeastern States, two species are so outstanding that they deserve to be treated apart from the rest. Both of these, the Catawba Rhododendron and the Flame Azalea, belong to the Ericaceae or Heath family. Although our eastern American species of azalea and rhododendron appear quite different, the botanically complex situation in the species of our western States and of Asia makes it seem wise to classify them in the same genus.

The Heath family, world-wide in distribution, contains such plants as heather, manzanita, mountain laurel, and trailing arbutus. The 1,500 or more species vary in stature from large forest trees to plants so small that, when not in flower, they might easily be mistaken for dwarfish, trailing mosses.

Widespread and varied as they are, these plants cannot tolerate alkaline or limy soil. Apparently this is because fungus threads (actually the plant body of various forest mushrooms) are associated with the roots of the members of this group, and without their help the plants cannot live. Since these fungi thrive only in acid soils, this family will grow in alkaline or calcareous regions only after extensive and costly treatment and preparation of the soil.

For more than a quarter-century I have been searching the Western Hemisphere, especially for members of the Heath family, and have seen many wondrous displays beside the trail. Yet in sheer magnificence nothing has approached the two species shown, when growing naturally in our southern Appalachians.

CATAWBA RHODODENDRON (*Rhododendron catawbiense*):
One day on a rocky trail on the divide near the headwaters of the Catawba I stopped to view the magnificent rolling crest of the Blue Ridge. Stretching ahead for nearly two

miles and cascading down the slope for a vertical distance of more than 500 feet was a nearly pure stand of this rhododendron in full bloom!

British gardeners really know their rhododendrons because, with both favorable climate and soil, they can cultivate not only our species but also Asiatic ones. In *Trees and Shrubs Hardy in the British Isles*, by that great English authority, W. J. Bean, we are told that the Catawba Rhododendron "has proved perhaps the most valuable evergreen shrub for ornament ever introduced." I wonder what the usually cautious Mr. Bean would have added had he seen the display in the spruce-rimmed glades at the Catawba's headwaters, or on Grandfather Mountain, Roan Mountain, or in the Great Smokies.

While some unusual color forms are derived by hybridization with Asiatic species, the hardiness and profusion of bloom in the best of our garden rhododendrons come from this parent.

FLAME AZALEA (*Rhododendron calendulaceum*):
Having seen and studied the Flame Azalea many times in the southern Appalachians, especially in the Cumberlands where it seems to reach a peak of coloring, I cannot trust myself to mention it in a detached or prosaic manner. In his book, *Ornamental American Shrubs*, Van Dersal rates the Flame Azalea as the finest shrub in the United States "because of the brilliant intensity of its flower color and its gorgeous display in bloom."

Excellent, my friend! But lest either of us be accused of playing favorites we will turn again to the experienced Mr. Bean, for his judgment was unprejudiced. Of the Flame Azalea he pithily remarked: "This is the most brilliantly coloured of all wild azaleas."

In the hands of the hybridist and selector, and blended with species from other lands, both the Flame Azalea and the Catawba Rhododendron have given rise to a host of glorious color forms. Grown singly beside a cottage door, in serried ranks on a great estate, or in massed profusion in a public park, they can hold their heads proudly erect, for they are among the choicest blooms in that great parade of flowering plants which brings the whole world into our gardens.

Descendants of Two Outstanding Native Americans Burgeon on a Majestic Estate. When June comes to the southern Appalachians prodigal Nature cloaks the mountainsides with flowers of Catawba Rhododendron (left). This hardy shrub is the basic parent of most of our showy modern garden forms. Flame Azalea (right) is considered one of America's finest flowering shrubs.

Our Vegetable Travelers

BY VICTOR R. BOSWELL

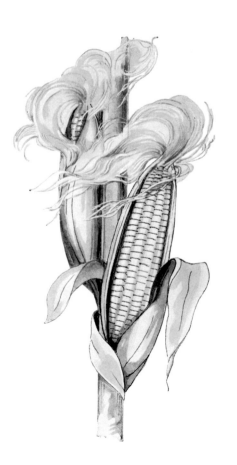

MY FRIEND'S GARDEN was only a tiny one in his back yard, but he was as proud of it as if it had been a farm. Noting my surprise at the uselessly small amounts of dozens of vegetables, he explained that, being a city dweller, he had seen vegetables only in stores and on the table and had been curious to see "how all those things grow."

"So far, I've grown only American vegetables," he said. "Next year I want to go in for foreign things. Do you know where I can get seeds?"

Glancing over his jumble of plants, I said: "Those tomatoes, snap beans, peppers, lima beans, and potatoes are the only truly American vegetables you have. All the others are foreign—onions, radishes, lettuce, spinach, beets, chard, cabbage, broccoli, collards, carrots, parsley, turnips, peas, asparagus, soybeans, mustard, eggplant, and the rest. The foreign plants in your garden outnumber the native ones five to one."

"What do you mean, 'foreign'?" he asked. "I bought the seed right here in town. I eat these vegetables every day."

"Yes, they're common to us," I agreed, "but their ancestors were foreigners to America, the same as your ancestors and mine."

Thus my friend became interested in the origins and travels as well as the growing habits of plants; he now includes plant history as part of his hobby.

His new-found interest actually has been shared for centuries by archeologists, historians, geographers, botanists, and others who have sought to find out where our vegetables came from, and where and when they were first used for food.

The early students of plant origins had only folk tales, sketchy records of travelers, and old writings to help them. Such sources gave a few valuable clues, but no proof of origin.

As prehistoric peoples moved about, even from one continent to another over land bridges or short stretches of water, they sometimes carried with them seeds of plants they had learned to use for food. By the time the oldest known records were written or carved, many plants were known over relatively vast stretches of the earth, particularly in Eurasia and parts of Africa.

This wide scattering of vegetable plants at the very dawn of history complicates the task of determining the exact region where they were first used as food. Because some vegetable has been known from the beginnings of history in widely separated lands, the people in each of those lands believed the plant to have originated there. Modern research has shown many such beliefs to be wrong.

Today shrewd scientific detectives are still at the job, seeking to define with ever-increasing exactness where this or that species originated. They are driven on by a practical purpose: to determine where plant-hunting expeditions are most likely to find cultivated or wild forms, or even closely related species, having characteristics that might be valuable in improving our crops through breeding.

One of the best evidences of origin of a cultivated plant is finding the place where its ancestral forms are still growing in the wild. For example, when explorer David Livingstone discovered wild watermelons growing profusely in central Africa, he solved the riddle of that plant's origin.

Sometimes, however, a wild plant is introduced into a new land where it continues to grow wild. Wild carrot grows over much of the United States, but it is not native here. And wild forms of many important crops have never been found anywhere. Maize (Americans call it "corn") is an illustration. Either its wild parent has vanished from the earth or has become isolated in remote areas of the South American lowlands.

Most botanists now agree that the region having the greatest *diversity* of forms of a given plant is its probable center of origin. The variety of wild and cultivated species of the potato found in the Andean region of South America, for example, points to this general region as its native home.

Names, too, help the plant historian. The presence of many names for a single plant among widely scattered tribes in a primitive country indicates the plant's antiquity in that area. If there is no such multiplicity of names in languages of other lands, the plant is probably native to the land where it has many.

When the white man first came, he found our common bean (*Phaseolus vulgaris*) widespread in North, Central, and South America; each tribe that grew it had its own name for the bean. It was called *sahe* or *sahu* by Indians on the St. Lawrence River; *ogaressa* by the Hurons; *tuppuhguam-ash* by northern Algonquins; *malachxil* by the Delawares; *okindgier* by Indians on the Roanoke River; *ayacotli* and *etl* by the Aztecs. Each tribe had grown this bean "always," as far back as their folk tales could tell them.

Many kinds of beans were known in the Old World, but no descriptions or names for this particular one existed in Old World languages until after Columbus's voyages. Since then our American type has been spread all over the globe. The Chinese have grown so many forms of this species that one authority has designated China a "secondary center of origin or distribution."

Other American vegetable species, too, were so quickly scattered over the earth after about 1500 and grown so extensively that for many years their American origin was overlooked. The sweet potato and the garden pepper are among those that were believed to be of Oriental origin.

Former confusion over these New World plants shows how easy it has been to lose sight of even the hemisphere of origin of certain plants just within the past few centuries. Imagine the difficulty of tracing Old World plants back to the country of their origin after they had been shuttled about Eurasia and Africa for thousands of years!

On this problem, archeologists' findings have been of considerable help. Ancient carvings, stone records, ornaments, and decorated utensils depicting food plants have been unearthed in tombs and dwelling sites in many parts of the world. Even the fragile remnants of ancient varieties of vegetable seeds have been found, thousands of years old. The seeds could be identified but, contrary to recurring tales, would *not* grow, for the life had long since gone out of them. One such story arose when grain seeds found in Egyptian mummy wrappings were planted, and did grow. It was later discovered that these seeds came from fresh, incompletely threshed straw used to pack the mummy for shipment.

In recent years the microscope has successfully been used in heredity studies in trying to ferret out obscure characteristics of related species that may be native to different regions. We can now confirm the supposed origin of

some plants with reasonable certainty by the shapes of the chromosomes—those minute structures within the cell which are the seat of the plant's hereditary mechanism.

For example, although maize almost certainly originated in South America, our North American types have chromosomes more like those of Central America's maize than Peru's. Our North American corn thus appears to be directly descended from Central American forms. The latter, in turn, resulted from prehistoric hybridization of South American maize with a related wild Central American plant having the same ancestor as maize.

Investigators constantly seek to learn more about human progress before history began. Civilizations rose, flourished, and disappeared, leaving only circumstantial evidence as to what happened to them. What did the people of those cities eat? Where did their food plants come from? Were those plants wild or cultivated? There must have been an agriculture, since cities cannot feed themselves on wild plants and game alone.

Agriculture, the purposeful rearing of animals and the cultivating of plants, began to develop in the last part of the Stone Age, when man learned also how to make pottery and how to sharpen tools by grinding rather than chipping. It did not come about all over the inhabited world at the same time. (Some primitive cultures today have developed little if any beyond the Stone Age.)

Man's first agricultural efforts doubtless were directed to those plants which yielded palatable, easily stored seeds, or large, fleshy underground parts that could be left in the

World-traveled Vegetables Thrive in the Friendly Soil of an American Garden. Sprouting broccoli, with upper leaves cut away, surrenders its edible flower buds; it first grew in Asia Minor and Mediterranean lands. Kohlrabi and hard-heading cabbage from northern Europe are basket-mates of snap beans, native Americans.

W. J. Mead, USDA

soil from one season to the next and dug up when wanted. Highly perishable leafy vegetables and fleshy-fruited varieties came into cultivation later.

Of the eight or ten main centers of plant origin, the area about the eastern end of the Mediterranean Sea is usually credited with the most vegetables now grown in America. Among them are asparagus, beets, broccoli, cabbage, cauliflower, celery, endive, kale, lettuce, parsley, parsnips, and rhubarb. The area from Asia Minor to Egypt, with its wide range of climatic and soil conditions, was the prehistoric world's most heavily traveled corridor.

However, we cannot be sure that all plants apparently originating in this eastern Mediterranean region actually did so. Some may have been carried there by migrants from farther east or north. Cabbage, lettuce, beets, and parsley show other centers of origin or distribution in the Near East. Likewise, many vegetables, such as peas, Indian mustard, carrot, onion, and muskmelon, show centers in both the Near and the Middle East.

Although there were barriers to movement of prehistoric peoples within this vast area between the Mediterranean and the Himalayas, they were less formidable than barriers to the east and south. The migrating peoples certainly carried seeds with them.

Such must have been the case with the early inhabitants of Mesopotamia (the non-Semitic Sumerians) who developed an advanced civilization, with important cities and trade with other lands, even before 4000 B.C. Where they came from we don't know, but by about 2750 B.C. they had touched the Mediterranean.

Semitic peoples from the west invaded Mesopotamia, and then the Aryans pushed in from the east, each doubtless carrying seeds of their favorite food crops. Later the Aramaeans invaded the country from the northwest. In 539 B.C. the Persians took over.

W. J. Mead, USDA

Lenses Like a Jeweler's Aid a Tomato Breeder in His Delicate Task. At the Department of Agriculture's Plant Industry Station at Beltsville, Maryland, this scientist removes pollen-bearing anthers from a tomato flower. A day later he will cross-pollinate it with pollen from a selected parent. The result: a hybrid.

Thus peoples moved from west, north, and east for thousands of years, distributing not only themselves, their animals, and their plants, but ideas, religions, and cultures. So it is not surprising that many species have more than one center of development and that it is not possible to say with finality which center developed first.

Europe's first cultivated plants were western Asiatic in origin. This is understandable in view of the fact that early peoples of the Near

East either dominated or influenced the whole of Eurasia in prehistoric times, and indirectly, therefore, the rest of the world.

About the time the New Stone Age man of the Near East was pushing to the eastern Mediterranean, in the third millennium B.C., he was also moving through Asia Minor, across the Dardanelles, along the coast of the Black Sea, and into Europe's Danube basin. His arrival appears to have coincided with the first agriculture in eastern Europe. Migrations into the Aegean and middle Mediterranean, by water and by land, further distributed Asiatic plants into southern Europe.

While the Near East has given the United States more vegetables, the Far East and India have provided the world with a larger number of cultivated plants of all types than has any other area. In this region the Chinese center of plant origins, chiefly in central and western China, was the most prolific, and that of middle and eastern India next. Vegetables which originated in China and are now grown in America include mustards, radishes, Chinese cabbage, and soybeans.

The abundant evidence of late Stone Age man in China shows he lived in rude villages, hunted, fished, farmed, had domestic animals, and presumably used several vegetables cultivated today. But despite prehistoric contact between China and western Asia there is less evidence of plant diffusion between China and middle Asia than between the Mediterranean and middle Asia. Geographic barriers have tended to isolate China, seat of one of the oldest cultures in existence.

India has contributed many of the world's cultivated plants, but only three are important vegetables in America: cowpeas (black-eyed peas), eggplant, and cucumbers. In India's hazy prehistory there is far less evidence of migrations of peoples, cultures, and plants than in areas to the west. This helps to explain why the many vegetables and related crops originating in India are not more important elsewhere today.

While Malaya and Indochina have contributed many economic plants, few are vegetables and none is important in America.

Africa has contributed only two vegetables common to us, okra and watermelons, and Australia not a single one.

Important agricultural civilizations developed in the New World, but they had been so completely isolated that they made no evident contributions to Old World agriculture, arts, customs, thought, or racial composition before Columbus. Very soon after the voyages of Columbus and the Spanish explorers, however, the world was enriched by many important new food plants from the Americas, including maize, potatoes, sweet potatoes, tomatoes, peppers, squash, common beans, and lima beans.

By the time of the early American explorations, Eurasian civilizations were highly developed, with means of travel and methods of disseminating ideas and goods. Thus the finding of New World food plants was followed by world-wide exploitation at an almost explosive speed. Within some 200 years previously unknown American plants were becoming important foods on every continent.

Man first reached the Americas far back in the Stone Age by slow migration from eastern Asia. He came either by way of a land bridge then connecting Siberia and Alaska, or by rafts or skin boats across the present Bering Strait. He subsisted by hunting, fishing, and harvesting whatever food the wild plants might offer him. Since these early migrants were not farmers, it is improbable that they brought any Asiatic plants to America.

For untold generations this thin stream of man trickled through North America, the Isthmus of Panama, and ultimately the full length of South America. Groups stayed behind along the way, as in Central America, and evolved distinct tribal cultures. As these American Indians adjusted to their environments, they learned to use and even came to depend upon the wonderfully productive native plants found in their respective areas.

Maya Corn God Sows His Maize. His bag holds grains of the Maya staff of life; his hat, resembling a bishop's miter, is a conventionalized ear of corn. Face fastened to his back may represent a severed head or a mask of stone or wood. More than 1,200 years ago a Maya sculptor carved this scene on a 16-foot, 5½-ton stela found at Piedras Negras, Guatemala. It symbolizes the vital role corn played in the New World's ancient civilizations.

Sylvanus Griswold Morley, Carnegie Institution

Two distinct civilization centers developed, and both became main centers of origin of our present important native crop plants. One was in Central America, and the other in the Andean region in what is now southern Peru, Bolivia, and northern Chile.

The Central American area was probably mainly dependent first upon beans, sweet potatoes, squash, and pumpkins, while the early Andean people grew maize, potatoes, and tomatoes. But before the white man reached the New World, further diffusion of the people had distributed most of these crops over those parts of the Americas where they could be grown.

What did prehistoric man do to improve wild plants? And how are our modern plant scientists any better at improving plants than our prehistoric ancestors were?

Cultivated varieties differ from the wild forms from which they came only in small part because they are sown in rows, fertilized, weeded, and otherwise given favorable growing conditions. If all the seed of a wild form were to be planted, year after year, and given the best of care, the plants might grow somewhat larger or make larger yields, but they would still be wild plants.

The important distinction between wild and cultivated plants is that wild plants perpetuate themselves under conditions of chance pollination and natural selection only. Our cultivated plants are the result of generations of purposeful or unwitting selection by man. Man adds nothing to the hereditary make-up of the world of plants, but does take advantage of the endless diversity nature provides.

Prehistoric man noticed that some plants were better for his use than others, so naturally he chose their seeds to plant. He automatically practiced plant selection of a sort. Thus thousands of years of discarding the undesirable and propagating what is desirable to man developed our superior, cultivated plants. (But in getting certain qualities we have unintentionally sacrificed others, such as the ability to survive under adverse conditions.)

The modern plant breeder, by choice of parent plants, by controlling pollination, and by wise selection and testing of the plant offspring through successive generations, may obtain, in a few years, especially desired combinations of *existing* hereditary factors that might not be *found* in the wild in hundreds or even thousands of years. But he must first discover somewhere in the world the parent plants that already possess the hereditary factors needed.

Busy Flies Labor in Bag Prisons to Pollinate Onion Flowers. The plant breeder's first step in producing certain onion hybrids is to remove open flowers, possibly "tainted" with unknown pollen, from the flower head of a pollen-sterile kind. He then encloses the remaining buds in a cellophane, paper, or cloth bag together with a flower head bearing the desired pollen. Ordinary blue blowflies placed in the bag move about, transferring pollen from one parent to the other when the buds open.

Purdy, USDA

The geneticist creates no new factors, but does invaluable rearranging of existing ones. He is rapidly finding factors that no one has known about, and he learns how they are inherited, so that plant improvement can be carried forward speedily.

The art and practice of plant improvement goes back to prehistoric times, but the science of *how* specific characters are inherited was born since the birth of many men now living. We could still make plant progress without the science of genetics, but it would be too slow and costly.

The improved strains produced by geneticists and plant breeders no doubt have played a part in making Americans the great vegetable eaters—and growers—we are today. Our use of fresh, canned, and frozen vegetables (except potatoes and sweet potatoes) has increased steadily for more than 30 years, while our use of potatoes and grains has dropped. Our small truck gardens near town and city are giving way to huge, more distant truck farms yielding crops by the acre, the ton, and the carload.

The expression "truck crops," incidentally, has no connection with the fact that they are commonly hauled to market in trucks. It derives from the French word *troquer*, meaning to barter or exchange, and in this country became synonymous with vegetables in general because much of this produce used to be bartered or sold in small lots. Today vegetables are big business.

What is a vegetable, exactly? What is the difference between a fruit and a vegetable? Is a tomato a fruit or is it a vegetable?

In 1893 an importer argued before the United States Supreme Court that tomatoes were fruit, and hence not subject to duty. The court held the tomato to be a vegetable because it was usually served at dinner in, with, or after the soup, or with fish or meats that constitute the main part of the meal.

For years, however, much more of America's annual crop has been canned as juice than as whole tomatoes; we now drink a major part of our tomatoes *before* the main part of any meal, as we drink a large share of our orange and grapefruit crops. Many tomatoes today also are made into preserves with sugar, or eaten raw, like fruits. Nevertheless, the tomato is legally a vegetable.

Of course, by botanical definition the tomato is a fruit—as are the snap or green bean, the pod of peas, the garden pepper, and the okra pod. Still, no one doubts they are vegetables. Again, the cucumber and the muskmelon belong to the same genus, *Cucumis*. They are similar in growth habits and in structure and both are eaten raw. Yet we say, simply as a matter of custom, that cucumbers are vegetables and muskmelons are fruits!

Thus it is evident that no clear-cut distinction exists between plants called vegetables and those called fruits. Generally speaking, however, we classify as vegetables those annual plants of which the immature succulent roots, bulbs, stems, blossoms, leaves, seeds, or fruits are eaten; also those perennial non-woody plants of which the roots, stems, leaf stalks, or leaves are eaten.

When the accompanying paintings were in preparation, a major problem confronted the artist: few vegetables can be shown in detail as they grow in the garden. To portray the principal features of certain vegetables, Mrs. Bostelmann has had to remove part of their leaves, to dig roots and tubers from the soil, to take only a branch of this, to pile the fruits of some, and to reduce others in size. The harvest stage as well as the flowering or seed-bearing stages of some leafy salad plants are shown on the same plate, although these occur months apart.

Only by such devices can the artist compress such a wealth of information into so little space and in such a beautiful manner.

World's No. 1 Vegetable

THE POTATO is doubtless the most important single vegetable in the world today. The word is believed to be derived from the Spanish discoverers' understanding of the South American Indian name for the plant, *papa* or *patata*.

Over most of the United States, "potato" refers to *Solanum tuberosum*, the white or "Irish" potato, although in many parts of our South the term means sweet potato.

As to where our cultivated potato originated, no one can say more definitely than that it came from the Andean part of South America. Unfortunately the white discoverers of Peru, Ecuador, and Chile were so bent on their quest for precious metals and stones that none considered the potato—far more valuable to mankind—important enough to record definite facts about it.

Efforts to trace the history of the plant suggest Chile as the country of origin. Many wild species grow in the cool parts of Peru, Bolivia, and Ecuador, but they seem generally more distantly related to our potato than those now found along the coast and islands of mid-southern Chile.

Some have believed that the Incas improved the wild, bitter potato of Peru to make it one of the mainstays of their life, along with maize. More likely, however, the potato they used was carried to their area from Chile by prehistoric tribes hundreds or thousands of years earlier.

When first encountered by the white man, the Indians of the high country of Peru preserved potatoes by drying them in the sun, a method still used. At high elevations in southern Peru the potatoes are exposed to freezing, after which they dry more rapidly. The dehydrated product might not be acceptable to us, but it meets the Indians' needs and can be kept from one harvest to the next, to be pounded into flour or cooked whole. Remains of prehistoric stores of these dried potatoes have been found.

Indications are that the potato was unknown in Central or North America or the West Indies until Pizarro conquered Peru. The references to "batatas" in accounts of the voyages of Columbus and Magellan indicate sweet potatoes rather than white potatoes. Thus it seems possible that the white man first carried the potato out of its South American home to the other Americas, as well as to Europe and elsewhere.

One story holds that Sir John Hawkins introduced the potato into Ireland in 1565; another says Sir Walter Raleigh first grew it there in 1585. In any case, it became important in Ireland before it did in other European countries or their American colonies. Stories of it being found in Virginia when first visited by the English are now believed to be due to confusion with another tuber-bearing plant.

The plant became firmly identified with Ireland; hence our common name, "Irish potato." During the 17th and 18th centuries the potato was gradually introduced into most other countries where it is now grown. It was brought to New England in 1719 by Irish immigrants who settled at Londonderry, New Hampshire. The kinds grown then were not nearly so productive or good to eat as modern varieties.

The potato gained popularity in northern Europe slowly before the grain famine there in 1770 compelled its use. A French leader of that period virtually forced the potato upon the underfed people through the soup kitchens he set up. Commemorating his work, potato soup bears his name: Parmentier.

By mid-19th century the potato was an important staple crop in northern Europe, the British Isles, North America, and to a less extent elsewhere. It formed such a large part of Ireland's food that an 1846–47 epidemic of potato late blight resulted in serious famine there.

Most Oriental peoples have never cared much for potatoes and have not learned to grow and to adapt them to their conditions. Soon after World War II, in studying vegetables in Japan, I was amazed to find the state of potato culture far below that of most other food plants, although it has been known there some 200 years.

Western South America Enriched the World with the Lowly Potato. Blinded by gold lust, the Conquistadores virtually ignored this native food plant, destined to feed huge populations and far exceed in value all the gold of the Incas. The potato's flowers are familiar to many, but few have seen its small seedy green fruits.

As American as Apple Pie

SWEET CORN (*Zea mays* variety *saccharata*) is a sugary-seeded kind of maize, as the "saccharin" part of its scientific name indicates. The old Anglo-Saxon word "corn" means grain of any kind, and except in the United States it does not refer specifically to Indian corn, *Zea mays*. The American Indian word "maize," however, is understood the world around.

Maize apparently went through its first great period of development in the Andes, probably in southern Peru, where primitive, but not wild, forms are still grown. No one has ever found wild maize or the wild parent from which it came.

Far back in prehistory, we believe, somewhere in the lowlands east of the Andes, the unknown parent of maize gave rise to a new and distinct parent form by mutation, producing a maize in which each seed was separately enclosed in husks. That particular "pod" corn was unlike modern pod corns. It occurred so long ago that the Indians now have no name for it, and it has never been found, though representations of it appear on ancient Peruvian pottery.

Later it mutated again to a form without husks around each seed.

While this maize was first developing into an important food crop in the Andean region, there probably was no maize in Central or North America. Growing wild, however, was a rather distinct relative of maize, now called *Tripsacum*, that may have arisen from the same member of the grass family. When the Indians from the Andes carried their primitive maize to Central America, it somehow became hybridized with this kindred plant, *Tripsacum*. The new hybrid persisted and has been named "teosinte."

Teosinte, in turn, became crossed with maize, one of its own parents. The descendants of this cross ultimately gave rise to several kinds of corn never known in the Andean region: pointed popcorn, dent corn (our commonest kind), flour corn, and flint corn. Thus the Central and North American forms of maize most likely developed, different to this day from forms grown in Peru.

After the new type arose, presumably in what is now Guatemala, it was carried up into the present southwestern United States and thence north and east over its present North American range. Before the white man reached America, most Indian tribes commonly grew maize of one kind or another except sweet corn. The sugary character in maize doubtless occurred innumerable times as a mutation, but many Indian tribes either disliked it or had trouble perpetuating it. (It is harder to produce and preserve the seed of sweet corn than that of other forms.)

A few tribes, among them the Hidatsa, Mandan, Omaha, Pawnee, Ponca, and Iroquois, have been known to grow sweet corn in North America, and apparently it was known in Peru in prehistoric as well as modern times. Yet it never became important even in North America until after the white man's arrival. Its first published mention was in 1801, and not until about 100 years ago did seedsmen in eastern States begin to list a variety or two. Since 1865 its popularity has grown steadily.

Now there is a wide range of kinds of sweet corn, from little four-inch ears growing on plants only two and a half feet high up to seven- or eight-inch ears on plants as tall as eight feet; white, yellow, purple kernels; white cobs, red cobs; ears with 8, 10, 12, or more rows of kernels—or with kernels not in rows at all. Among the best-known ordinary varieties are Golden Bantam, Country Gentleman, and Stowell's Evergreen.

Our modern hybrid sweet corns, such as Golden Cross Bantam, Ioana, Marcross, and scores of others, were developed by painstaking effort. The basic discoveries concerning hybrid vigor were made more than 50 years ago, but it took breeders some 20 years to put hybrid corn production on a profitable, practical basis.

Each lot of today's hybrid seed is the result of a controlled cross between two especially developed parents. Most of the seed sweet corn planted now is of the hybrid type.

Today's Sweet Corn Descends from Maize Grown on Andean Slopes. Maize, a gigantic grass whose wild ancestor has never been found, sustained the remarkable pre-Columbian civilizations of the Americas. Sweet corn, important only in the past 100 years, is now grown in yellow, white, "black" (dark purple), and reddish kinds.

109

Two New Beans from America

BEFORE COLUMBUS, the Old World was familiar with many kinds of beans, but knew neither our common bean, *Phaseolus vulgaris*, nor the lima bean, *P. lunatus*. Their American origin is fixed by descriptions and references to finding them at widely scattered points in the Americas about 1500 and soon after.

The word "bean," like "vegetable," is indefinite; it refers to the seeds of many plants. Our expression "common bean" agrees in meaning with the scientific name, *Phaseolus vulgaris*. It includes our dry, field varieties such as Navy or Pea Bean, Red Kidney, Pinto, Great Northern, Marrow, and Yellow Eye. It also includes all our edible-podded garden beans called stringless or snap beans and formerly called string beans. (Some varieties *are* stringy.)

The English first used the name "kidney bean" in 1551 to distinguish our American common bean from Old World types.

In the South and some other parts of this country lima beans are called butter beans, a term sometimes used in New England for yellow-podded ("wax") varieties of snap beans.

Not long ago Brazil was believed to be the country of origin of lima beans, but new evidence points to Guatemala. Wild primitive lima beans have been found there, along with many cultivated forms. Their distribution from Guatemala has been traced by the prehistoric varieties left along Indian trade routes.

One "bean migration" extended up through Mexico into what is now our Southwest, thence eastward to spread from Florida to Virginia, with types varying from the present small lima beans used by the Hopi Indians in the Southwest to the Sieva type found in the East. Another course extended down through Central America into Peru, where large-seeded, large-podded types were developed in warm coastal

Indians Carried Common and Lima Beans into Both Continents from Central America. Europe knew neither species before Columbus. Common beans (top) include "wax"-pod and green-pod snap varieties, kidney and "pea" beans. Lima beans (bottom) were named for Lima, Peru; they are now believed native to Guatemala.

areas. The name "lima bean" came from Lima, Peru, one point at which early European explorers found the species.

A third, but less extensive, branch of development extended eastward through the West Indies and thence southward toward the mainland of South America. Some Caribbean types tend to develop poisonous quantities of cyanide under certain conditions. These "bad actors" are generally very small, nearly round, and often are hardly recognizable as lima beans.

There is an almost endless diversity of seed sizes, shapes, and color combinations among the lima beans, although few colored varieties are now grown in the United States. Bush varieties have been developed since 1875, but the dwarf mutation on which they are based had doubtless occurred many times before.

Since dry common and lima beans are highly concentrated foods, easily carried and stored, explorers and slavers of the early 1500's found them ideal for ships' provisions. Obtained from Indians in many places in the Americas, they were carried to the ends of the earth. By the late 1700's the lima bean was reported in Europe, Africa, the East Indies, India, and the Philippines. In Europe it apparently was first recorded about 1591, but since it requires warm weather for good growth, it is less important there than the common bean.

The common bean also is believed native to Central America and probably was similarly distributed. Because of its greater range of cultivation when discovered, and its greater diversity in North America, probably its culture is even older than that of the lima bean.

When the white man arrived, climbing beans were generally planted along with maize all over the Americas. Maize is high in starch, while beans are high in proteins. Combined in succotash (an Indian invention), they met most of the nutritive requirements of those tribes that used little or no meat.

The pods of some forms were eaten in the green state, at least by white men, virtually from the time of their discovery. Today's truly stringless, nearly fiberless, tender-podded varieties were developed less than a hundred years ago.

111

The Tomato Had to Go Abroad to Make Good

ONE OF THE STRANGEST things about the history of the tomato (*Lycopersicon esculentum*) is the fact that, although it is of American origin, it was unknown as food in this country until long after it was commonly eaten in Europe. Until hardly more than a century ago it was generally thought here to be poisonous and was grown only as an ornamental garden plant.

The mistaken idea that tomatoes were poisonous probably arose because the plant belongs to the Nightshade family, of which some species are truly poisonous. The strong odor of the leaves and stems also contributed to the idea that the fruits were unfit for food.

Our word "tomato" is but a slight modification of *tomati*, the name used by the Indians of Mexico, who have grown the plant for food since prehistoric times. Early European explorers also recorded *tomatl*, *tumatle*, and *tomatas*, probably variants of Indian words.

Tomatoes apparently originated as wild forms in the Peru-Ecuador-Bolivia area of the Andes. Many forms, wild and cultivated, abound there today in moderate altitudes. The cultivated tomato is very tender to cold and intolerant of extremely hot or dry weather, a characteristic reflecting its native climate.

Presumably the cultivated tomato was carried

Indians Grew Many Kinds of Tomatoes for Food Before Columbus. White men, however, long regarded the "love apple" as poisonous. These were originally cultivated in the Americas—small pear-shaped tomatoes, cherry-sized ones, large-fruited red and yellow kinds, and the tiny "currant" tomato.

grew it about 1550 and apparently were the first Europeans to eat it. About 25 years later it was grown in English, Spanish, and mid-European gardens, chiefly as a curiosity. The French named it *pomme d'amour*, hence the English and early American term "love apple."

One early Italian writer called the tomato *poma Peruviana*, suggesting that it was introduced from Peru. Another called it *poma d'oro*, or "gold apple," indicating that the earliest introductions were yellow-fruited. By the mid-18th century the tomato was grown for food not only in Italy but in many other European countries.

Not until after the Declaration of Independence do we find a record of the tomato as being grown in this country by white men. Thomas Jefferson, a progressive Virginia farmer as well as a statesman, grew it in 1781. A French refugee from Santo Domingo supposedly introduced it to Philadelphia in 1789, and an Italian painter to Salem, Massachusetts, in 1802.

Tomatoes were eaten in New Orleans as early as 1812, doubtless through French influence, but were not grown for food in our Northeast for another 20 to 25 years. The shapes and colors in the States today were found by the earliest explorers. Plant breeders have greatly improved fruit size, smoothness, and yield.

As a food of world-wide importance, the tomato is about the newest. It has been cultivated and bred so assiduously in Europe that European varieties now contribute important characters for improving the United States crop. Italy has long been famous for its tomato paste, made from small, oblong, rich, red fruit; and spaghetti is hardly spaghetti without tomato sauce.

After having made good abroad, the tomato has attained great importance in its native hemisphere. Today, millions of tons of tomatoes are grown in the United States alone.

from the Andes into Central America and Mexico, as was maize, by a prehistoric migration of Indians. Since comparatively few primitive forms are found in Central America and Mexico, this probably occurred in relatively recent times—perhaps in the last 2,000 years.

It seems likely that the tomato, because of its highly perishable fruit, was among the last of the native plants to be cultivated as food by the Indians. Lack of evidence of its use by North American Indians further suggests its rather late movement from South America.

For more than 200 years after 1554, when the first known record of the tomato was written, it was gradually carried over the globe. European writers mention seeing it in far places, but not in what is now the United States. Italians first

Sweet Potato, Another American

THE SWEET POTATO (*Ipomoea batatas*) is another of the native American plants found by Columbus and his shipmates. Although it was probably found in the West Indies on the earlier voyages, it is not definitely mentioned in their records until the fourth voyage.

In the islands off the coast of Yucatán and Honduras the sweet potato was called *axi* and *batatas* or *betatas* by the natives; in 1514, Peter Martyr named nine Honduran varieties. It was taken to Spain about 1500 and several kinds, including red, purple, and "white," were cultivated there by the mid-16th century.

Sweet potato cultivation was tried unsuccessfully in Belgium in 1576. John Gerarde claimed that in 1597 he grew the plant in England (probably with little success) and that it was known in India, Barbary, and other hot regions.

Early Spanish explorers are believed to have taken the sweet potato to the Philippines and East Indies, from which Portuguese voyagers soon carried it to India, China, and Malaya. The original introductions from America into the Pacific and Far East were so unobtrusive that many believed it native to Asia.

The sweet potato, because it thrives in a hot, moist climate, has never become as popular in Europe as the Irish potato; it still is little known even in the warmer Mediterranean areas. But in subtropical and tropical areas it is far more important: in the Pacific islands, the East Indies, India, China, and in Japan, where it is now one of the most important food crops.

Apparently it was introduced to Kyushu from China around 1700, by way of the Ryukyu Islands. This late date seems in itself a good argument against its Chinese or other Asiatic origin. In southern Kyushu today it is commonly called *kara-imo*, meaning Chinese potato; but elsewhere in Japan it is called *satsuma-imo*, Japanese potato.

In the past 30-odd years, plant breeders in Australia and the warmer parts of Russia have sought to develop its culture on a large scale.

Sweet potatoes were cultivated in Virginia in 1648, possibly earlier, and are said to have been taken into New England in 1764. Indians of our South grew them in the 18th century,

but we do not know how much earlier. In the South today they are generally preferred to Irish potatoes as staple food; in the North the reverse is true. Generally speaking, northerners prefer the so-called "dry-fleshed" sweet potato. such as Big Stem Jersey and Little Stem Jersey, while southerners prefer the "moist-fleshed" type (which actually contains less water), such as the Porto Rico and related varieties. The soft, rich "moist" varieties are erroneously called "yams" in the United States; the yam is an entirely different plant, of the genus *Dioscorea*, and is still a curiosity in this country.

The flesh of most sweet potato varieties is white or nearly so, although in the United States we prefer yellow- or orange-fleshed varieties because of their valuable carotene (provitamin A) content. Some kinds have purple flesh, but they are not grown here. Skin colors range from nearly white through shades of buff to brown or through pink to copper, even magenta and purple. Americans are prejudiced against the latter because certain "red" varieties formerly grown here were of poor quality.

In our northern States the sweet potato is used only as human food, and to only a small extent. In the South much of the crop is fed to livestock, and breeders have produced new large-yield varieties for stock feed or industrial use. The sweet potato generally contains more starch than the Irish potato, but is too costly as yet to produce especially for starch manufacture. Sweet potato candies, ice cream, cookies, and related delicacies are surprisingly good.

The sweet potato rarely flowers under ordinary field conditions and more rarely sets seed in the Temperate Zones. Thus breeders in Japan or the United States must resort to special greenhouse culture, or even send parent varieties to the Tropics for flowering and hybridization.

Earliest Voyagers to Tropical America Found Sweet Potatoes. Europeans first saw these nuggets of tasty, golden root in the West Indies, some years before they found the white potato in the Andes. Sweet potato blooms freely in the Tropics, rarely in the north. Its flowers resemble those of the related morning glory.

Squash Named from an Indian Word

OUR WORD SQUASH comes from the Massachuset Indian word *askutasquash*, meaning "eaten raw or uncooked." Although the Indians may have eaten some forms of squash raw, today we like our squashes cooked.

The late-growing, less symmetrical, odd-shaped, rough or warty kinds, small to medium in size, but with long-keeping qualities and hard rinds, are usually called winter squash. They belong almost without exception to the species *Cucurbita maxima* or *C. moschata*. The small, quick-growing forms that are eaten before the rinds and seeds harden are called summer squash and belong to the species *C. pepo* (page 118).

Pumpkins also belong to the latter species, but large, late, smooth, symmetrical forms of *C.* *maxima* and *C. moschata* sometimes are called pumpkins regardless of species. The word "pumpkin" (mispronounced "punkin" by many Americans, including myself) comes from the old French term *pompion*, meaning eaten when "cooked by the sun," or ripe. In modern French, pumpkin is called *potiron*.

All three species of squashes and pumpkins are native to the Western Hemisphere. *C. maxima*, represented now by such varieties as Hubbard, Delicious, Marblehead, Boston Marrow, and Turks Turban, apparently originated in northern Argentina near the Andes, or in certain Andean valleys. When Spanish conquerors found it there, this species, unlike maize and tomatoes, had not been carried into Central or

North America or even northern South America. It was unknown to the Old World until the 16th century, the oldest record dating from 1591.

Since *C. maxima* requires a fair amount of hot weather for best growth, it is not well known in northern Europe, the British Isles, or similar areas with short or cool summers. Only long-vining plants are known in this species.

C. moschata, represented by such varieties as Cushaw and Winter Crookneck squashes, and Japanese Pie and Large Cheese pumpkins, is a long-vining plant native, like *C. pepo*, to Mexico and Central America. As food plants in these areas they rank next to maize and beans; in some regions the flowers and mature seeds are eaten, as well as the flesh of the fruit.

Before the advent of the white man, *C. moschata* and *C. pepo* had been carried over all parts of North America where they could be grown, but they had not been carried into South America as had beans, which originated in the same general region. Indian tribes grew them generally throughout what is now the United States. Many of these tribes, particularly in the West, still grow a diversity of hardy squashes and pumpkins not found in our markets.

Although winter squashes are grown in many lands today, they are relatively unimportant with few exceptions. They are grown extensively in tropical America, in Japan, and in certain districts in the United States. The calabazas of the West Indies and the forms grown by the natives of Mexico and Central America are not the uniform, pure varieties we grow but vary widely in size, shape, color, and quality. Since these species are normally cross-pollinated, it is difficult to keep a variety pure.

In Japan just after World War II, I found squash growing on trellises over the doorways or on the sides of houses, at the foundations of burned-out buildings with vines growing over the ruins, and beside and over small streams on horizontal trellises of poles.

The largest "pumpkins" grown and bragged about are often *C. maxima*, really squashes; they furnish much of our pumpkin pie. The best commercially canned "pumpkin" actually is Delicious, Boston Marrow, or similar squash. Their flesh is much richer and more nutritious than that of pumpkin.

Some years ago a North Dakota horticulturist bred a small variety of turban squash as a substitute for the sweet potato, which does not thrive on the northern Great Plains. This little Buttercup squash has flesh surprisingly similar to the sweet potato in taste and quality.

Hard-shelled Winter Squash Was an Important American Indian Food. Borne on trailing vines, the large Hubbard, Delicious, Cushaw, and Turks Turban (left to right) are long-keeping kinds; the small Acorn (left) is more akin to the summer squashes. Much "pumpkin pie" we eat is really made with squash.

Summer Squash Is Best When Harvested Early

SUMMER SQUASH varieties (*C. pepo*) are properly harvested for food while tender and immature, before either the seeds or the rinds have become firm or tough.

The fruits are cooked with no prior preparation except washing and perhaps cutting into pieces of convenient size. In English-speaking countries other than the United States, they are generally called vegetable marrows.

This kind is apparently the one most frequently described as "squash" by European visitors to our Atlantic coast during the 17th century, though observers in the preceding century had referred to this type as a kind of gourd because of its superficial resemblance to Old World gourds.

A vining variety introduced as new in America in 1881 happened to be exactly like one described in Germany in 1552 and recognized as of American origin. Fruits like our present White Bush Scallop or Cymling were accurately illustrated by the French botanist Matthias Lobel in 1591, and the bush form of squash was known in Europe in the 17th century, if not earlier.

The White Bush Scallop was called Symnel in 1648, but Thomas Jefferson, in 1803, wrote it "Cymling," the commonest name for it in our South today. Our present Summer Crookneck, named in seed catalogues as early as 1828, appears to be the same as a squash Champlain described in 1605.

Thus it seems that the culture and use of summer squashes has been well known in Europe since our earliest colonial times. Both European and American gardeners still grow many varieties that are substantially the same as those grown by pre-Columbian Indians. The summer squashes have long been popular in Italy, as indicated by the names and varieties developed there—Cocozelle and Zucchini, for example—which have become popular in America.

Because of the fantastic success of hybrid corn (maize) in recent decades, plant breeders have tried to increase yields of summer squash through hybridization, with some success. However, the pollen-bearing flowers must be removed from the seed-parent plants at short intervals, thus making hybrid squash seed costly as compared with hybrid corn seed. The object is to allow pollen-bearing flowers to develop only on those plants especially selected to furnish pollen, thus ensuring that the seed which forms on the seed-parent plants will be hybrid.

To be really good, the fruits of Cymling, Summer Crookneck, Summer Straightneck, Zucchini, and such varieties must be harvested (every two or three days in hot weather) while so young that the rind has not developed noticeably. It requires only four to six days after

bloom for a fruit of many of these varieties to reach the harvest stage. After two or three more days they are too old and tough to be desirable.

The American species of summer squash is grown to some extent in the warmer parts of Asia, but it is not well adapted to those lands. Orientals depend mainly on Asiatic forms of gourds for a product similar to our young summer squash fruit. These Asiatic gourds have not found favor in America because they are extremely rank-growing, late, and their fruits are considered here as less pleasing to the taste than our own squashes.

A few years ago there was developed an early, very small-fruited variety of pumpkin borne on plants like those of bush summer squash. It is called Cheyenne Bush Pumpkin and was bred for adaptation to the short season and low average

Summer Squash and a Relative, the Pumpkin, Are Also Native Americans. Golden Summer Crookneck, Golden Summer Straightneck, Zucchini, Cocozelle, and White Bush Scallop (left to right at bottom) are all "bush" kinds, eaten when immature. The large field pumpkin is of the same species, but grows on long vines.

temperatures of the high plains east of the Rocky Mountains. The fruit is allowed to mature before use, as is that of most pumpkins.

This is perhaps as good a place as any to point out that *neither squash nor pumpkin will cross-pollinate either watermelon or muskmelon*. Bad weather, poor soil, or disease may make melons taste bad, but squash or pumpkins growing near-by will not make them lose quality or taste like pumpkin, despite the persistent belief to the contrary.

119

Garden Pepper, Both a Vegetable and a Condiment

THE GARDEN PEPPER (*Capsicum frutescens*) is not related to the true pepper (*Piper nigrum*) from which we get the common black pepper on our tables. Why do we call *C. frutescens* pepper?

When Columbus, on his quest for a short trade route to the spice-rich East, found the Indians of the West Indies growing and using fiery forms of *Capsicum*, he and his men thought the plant to be a kind of pepper.

As early as 1493 Peter Martyr wrote that Columbus brought home "pepper more pungent than that from the Caucasus." In 1494 the physician to Columbus's fleet on his second famous voyage referred to the plant in a letter to Spanish authorities; 20 years later another Spanish explorer fully described the plant and its uses.

This intense interest in the pungent forms of *Capsicum* from the very time of their discovery, accompanied by definite descriptive records, is unique in the history of American plants. While important plants such as the potato were long ignored, to the spice-conscious discoverers this pepper was an unexpected and welcome find.

Fragments of different types of peppers have been found in Peruvian ruins believed to be more than 2,000 years old. Fruits of the pepper are pictured in embroidery on an Indian garment unearthed near the coast of Peru and believed to date back to about the first century. The Olmecs, Toltecs, and Aztecs also are known to have cultivated and used peppers extensively. Voyagers in the early 16th century encountered

many forms of peppers wherever they touched the American Tropics—in the West Indies, Central America, Mexico, Peru, Chile. By the beginning of the 17th century they had found virtually every form known today, all being grown by the Indians. Mexicans and our southwestern Indians today eat almost incredible quantities of hot peppers; they use them fresh, both green and red ripe, and in the dried mature form.

Peppers were introduced into Spain in 1493, were known in England by 1548, and in Central Europe by 1585 or earlier. In the 17th century the Portuguese took them to India and southeastern Asia. Peppers became so common there that their American origin was long overlooked, even though in India they are called "chillies."

In Spain the hot peppers are called *chili* (from Chile) and certain hot kinds are called chili peppers in the United States. A mixture of chopped meat and beans, highly flavored with chili pepper, is called *chili con carne*—"chili with meat." The mild or sweet kinds in Spain are called *pimenta* or *pimiento*, while in the United States "Pimiento" refers to only a single type of thick-fleshed, bright-red sweet pepper. It yields the brilliant stuffing in olives, the red particles in pimento cheese, and the pimiento we buy in tiny cans or jars.

A distinctive form of long, thick, bright-red pepper with nonpungent flesh has long been cultivated in Hungary and adjacent areas under the name *paprika*. Paprika production in the United States is negligible. The tabasco pepper is the basis of the pungent tabasco sauces made in our South.

Cayenne pepper is the dried, ground fruit of a long, slender form of hot "red pepper." This form, named for a coastal city in French Guiana in South America, was doubtless taken to Asia by Spanish or Italian explorers and reintroduced into America from there.

All these forms are important commodities of trade and add zest to the world's cookery. In the United States, however, the nonpungent, large-fruited form has become by far the most extensively grown.

As a boy in the Middle West, I heard our large, sweet, garden peppers commonly called "mango peppers," a term rarely used in America today. Now when we say "peppers" without any qualifying word we usually mean sweet or nonpungent kinds that are eaten as a vegetable, either cooked or raw in salads. Large quantities today are being commercially preserved in brine, or even diced and dehydrated, for use in vegetable and salad mixtures after re-freshening.

Peppers, Valued as Spices, Were Discovered by Columbus. The hot kinds at right were especially prized by early voyagers, but now the large, sweet, bell-shaped and the conical Pimiento varieties are more popular in the United States. These plants are unrelated to that, native to Asia, which yields common black pepper.

Greeks and Romans Grew Kale and Collards

KALE AND COLLARDS are similar in many respects, differing in little more than leaf form. They are, in effect, primitive cabbages. More highly developed forms, such as cauliflower, broccoli, and head cabbage, have been produced in the last 2,000 years or so, but kales and collards have persisted, although primitive, because of their merits as garden vegetables.

These leafy nonheading cabbages bear the Latin name *Brassica oleracea* variety *acephala*, the last term meaning "without a head." Kale is often called borecole, and in America collards are sometimes called sprouts. Kale is a Scottish word derived from *coles* or *caulis*, terms the Greeks and Romans used in referring to the whole cabbagelike group of plants. The German word *Kohl* has the same origin. "Collards" is a corruption of *coleworts* or *colewyrts*, Anglo-Saxon terms meaning cabbage plants.

The cabbagelike plants are native to the eastern Mediterranean region or to Asia Minor but, because of long cultivation, and shifting about by prehistoric traders and migrating tribes, their exact place of origin is unknown. The original cabbage was undoubtedly a nonheading kind with a prominent stalk or stem, and the kales and collards are not far removed from it. Wild forms have become widely distributed, with many names in many languages, and are found as far from their place of origin as the coasts of northern Europe and Britain.

Apparently all of today's principal forms of kale and collards have been known for at least 2,000 years. The Greeks grew kale and collards, although they made no such distinction between them as we make today. Well before the Christian era the Romans grew mild-flavored kinds with large leaves and stalks; a crisp-leaved form; some with small stalks and small, sharp-tasting leaves; a broad-leaved form like collards; and others with curled leaves. "Coles" were also described by European writers in the first, third, fourth, and 13th centuries.

It might appear that the Romans carried the coles to Britain and France, since they knew the plants so well and the species had been popular in those countries for so long. Or they may have been taken there somewhat earlier by the Celts.

The first mention of the kales (coleworts) in America was in 1669; but because of their popularity in Europe it is probable they were introduced somewhat earlier. Although many forms of *Brassica oleracea* are now known in parts of the Orient, they are not nearly so popular as the Far Eastern species of *Brassica* (page 166).

Kale and collards have remained minor commercial crops in the United States, although collards are the standard winter greens in home gardens of the South. Neither crop thrives in hot weather, which gives the plants a strong, unattractive flavor. Cool growing weather, fall frosts, and mild winters impart a high sugar content and fine flavor. They are among the easiest of all vegetables to grow. They are biennials, putting up their flower or seed stalks in the spring of their second season of growth.

All varieties of collards appear rather similar, but the kales show interesting diversity: tall and short; highly curled and plain leaved; bluegreen, yellow-green, and red; erect and flatgrowing; and in various combinations and gradations of these characters.

Those who know both kale and collards usually consider the latter to be better eating. Nutrition experts in recent years have sought to popularize both plants because they are unusually rich in minerals and vitamins.

Before the "newer knowledge" of nutrition, our experts bemoaned the poor diet of southern farmers, especially the Negroes, and were amazed to find so many of those people to be apparently well nourished. The ubiquitous collard patch on farm and in dooryard is now believed to play a most important part in furnishing the necessary vitamins and minerals. On one truck farm I saw a beautiful 10-acre field of collards. The farmer explained that it was not for market, but "just a collard patch for the hired hands."

Kale (Left) and Collards (Right) Are the Most Primitive Cultivated Cabbages. These leafy, nonheading cabbages originated in the eastern Mediterranean and westernmost Asia. Rich in minerals and vitamins, they differ little from the wild forms of cabbage man first used for food in prehistoric times.

Of Cabbages and Celts

THE WORD "CABBAGE" is an Anglicized form of the French *caboche*, meaning head. It has been used freely to refer to loose-heading (or even nonheading) forms of *Brassica oleracea* as well as to the modern hard-heading type classified as *B. oleracea* variety *capitata*.

Introduction of cabbage into Europe has been generally ascribed to the Romans, but probably the Celts of central and western Europe, who had much to do with distributing and popularizing cabbage, introduced it even earlier. Evidence points to the eastern Mediterranean and Asia Minor as its place of origin, but Celtic knowledge of it was so ancient as to have influenced the Latin name, *Brassica* (from the Celtic word *bresic*, meaning cabbage).

The Celts invaded Mediterranean lands repeatedly from about 600 B.C. to the beginning of the Christian era, reaching into Asia Minor around 278 B.C. They also pushed into the British Isles in the fourth century B.C. Shortly before the Christian era the Romans spread into northern Europe and into Britain. Thus it is not surprising that the history of cabbagelike vegetables has been confused.

Most European and Asiatic names for cabbage can be traced to one of three Celtic or part-Celtic root words. *Kopf Kohl* (German), *cabus* and *caboche* (French), *cabbage* (English), *kappes*, *kraut*, *kapost* (Tartar), *kopi* (Hindu), and others, all are related to the Celto-Slavic *cap* or *kap*, meaning head. *Kaulion* (Greek), *caulis* (Latin), *kale* (Scottish), *kaal* (Norwegian), *kohl* (Swedish), *col* (Spanish), are related to the Celto-Germanic-Greek *caul*, meaning stem.

In southern Europe, Mediterranean peoples developed those forms of cabbage (not hard-heading) that are tolerant to warm climates; the hard-heading cabbages were developed in the cooler parts of Europe by peoples largely Celtic,

Head Cabbage Got Its Start in Southern Europe and Was Perfected Farther North. Loose-heading varieties originated in northwest Italy and southeast France; hard-heading kinds were developed in the Middle Ages in northern Europe, whence most United States varieties stem. The seed-bearing stage is shown at right.

Nordic, or both. Had there been a hard-heading variety in ancient Rome, the old Roman writers certainly would have noted and described it.

"White" (hard-heading) cabbages were apparently unknown until after the time of Charlemagne, who died A.D. 814. Albert of Cologne, in the 13th century, referred to a headed cabbage, and in 14th century England the words *cabaches* and *caboches* were used, indicating then a distinction between heading and nonheading cabbages (coleworts).

Not until 1536 in Europe were unmistakable descriptions of hard-heading cabbage recorded. A loose-heading form called *romanos*, and later called *chou d'Italie* and *chou de Savoys*, for the Italian province, was also described. This crumpled-leaved "savoy cabbage" of high quality was grown in England in the 1500's.

Jacques Cartier introduced cabbage to America in 1541-42, planting it in Canada on his third voyage. Though doubtless planted in this country by early American colonists, there is no written record of it until 1669; in the 18th century Indians also were growing it.

Hard-heading cabbage was unobserved in Japan as late as 1775, and is still of minor importance in the Orient. There are no Sanskrit or other ancient Eastern language names to indicate that it has been long in that area.

The round-headed form is the oldest of the hard type of cabbage and the only one described during the 16th century. In the 17th century, flat-headed and egg-shaped varieties appeared, and in the 18th century conical or pointed kinds. Germany, France, and the Low Countries produced the largest number of new varieties; most grown in the United States today originated there.

"Red" cabbage (magenta to purplish) was first described in England in 1570, all the early varieties being round-headed. Now there are red varieties in all the head shapes. The "red" color is confined to the "skin" of each leaf and stem; the cells beneath are green or white. Red varieties are popular in northern Europe and savoyed varieties in warmer parts of Europe. Most cabbage grown in this country, however, is of the smooth-leaved green or white kind.

Kohlrabi and Brussels Sprouts Are European

CERTAIN VEGETABLES of American origin have been called new in the sense that they have attained widespread importance in the last 200 years or so, although those plants were used for food in America for hundreds, even thousands, of years before its discovery.

Kohlrabi and brussels sprouts, however, apparently were unknown anywhere more than a mere 400 to 500 years ago. They appear to be *really* new, and the only common vegetables of North European origin.

Although kohlrabi (*Brassica oleracea* variety *caulo-rapa*) and brussels sprouts (*B. oleracea* variety *gemmifera*) appear radically different, they are horticultural forms or races of the same species, *Brassica oleracea*, to which common cabbage, kale, broccoli, and cauliflower belong. All have a common parent, wild cabbage.

"Kohlrabi" comes from the German, *Kohl* meaning cabbage and *Rabi* meaning turnip. This "cabbage" with a turniplike enlargement of the stem above ground apparently was developed in northern Europe not long before the 16th century. The marrow cabbage from which it probably came is a cold-tender, nonheading plant with a thick succulent stem, while kohlrabi as we know it is a hardy vegetable, evidently developed in a cool climate.

A European botanist first described kohlrabi in 1554. By the end of the 16th century it was known in Germany, England, Italy, Spain, Tripoli, and the eastern Mediterranean. It is said to have been first grown on a field scale in Ireland in 1734, in England in 1837. In the United States, records of its use go back to 1806.

The plant is easy to grow, remarkably productive, and an ideal garden vegetable, although some dislike its flavor, which is similar to that of the turnip but milder and sweeter if the vegetable is harvested while young and tender.

Two main types are grown in America, white and purple. The "white," actually light green, is the more popular although the purple variety is most attractive. In Europe, fancy kinds with frilled and deeply cut leaves are sometimes grown for ornament. Like other members of its species, kohlrabi is a biennial, requiring parts of two growing seasons, with a cool rest period (wintertime) between, to produce seed.

Brussels sprouts are so named partly because the plant is supposed to have been grown since time immemorial in the vicinity of Brussels in Belgium. Though it probably first attained importance in that area, or even was developed there, it has been known for only about 400 years. The first rough description of it was in 1587, and even some 17th century botanists referred to it without actually having seen it.

The plant is really a tall-stemmed cabbage in which many tiny heads ("sprouts") form along the stem at the bases of the leaves instead of making one large head at the top of a short stem. After a head of common cabbage is cut from its plant, numerous tiny heads often will grow from the stem in much the same manner.

Varieties range from short to tall, but are otherwise not strikingly different. The existence of so few forms and names supports the belief that the brussels sprouts is a new form botanically as well as agriculturally.

Since this plant is actually a form of cabbage, it will hybridize freely with common cabbage and other forms of the same species: kale, cauliflower, kohlrabi, broccoli, and collards. In producing seed for planting, cross-pollination with any of these is disastrous, because such seed will produce intermediate mixed offspring.

Because this plant is so new and so limited by its need for a long, cool growing season, its history has hardly begun. By 1800, however, it was commonly grown in Belgium and France, and by 1850 it was becoming popular in England, where it is in high favor today. Although known since about 1800 in America, it is neither common nor highly popular here. Most of our crop is produced on Long Island, New York.

Northern Europe Contributed These Two Members of the Cabbage Clan. Brussels sprouts (left) and kohlrabi (right) are the only vegetables that originated there, except possibly the rutabaga (page 140). Both date from the late Middle Ages and derive from wild cabbage brought to Europe from warm Mediterranean lands.

Cabbage Flowers for Food

BROCCOLI AND CAULIFLOWER are two more kinds of *Brassica oleracea*, so similar that both are designated as botanical variety *botrytis*, from a Greek word meaning a cluster like a bunch of grapes.

"Broccoli" is Italian taken from the Latin *brachium*, meaning an arm or branch. "Cauliflower" comes from the Latin terms *caulis* (cabbage) and *floris* (flower). These "cabbages" are grown for their thickened, undeveloped flowers and flower stalks, not for their leaves.

Broccoli has two distinct forms. One has a dense, white "curd" like that of cauliflower and is called heading broccoli or cauliflower broccoli. The other has a somewhat branching cluster of green flower buds atop a thick, green flower stalk two to two and a half feet tall, and smaller clusters that arise like sprouts from the stems at the attachments of the leaves. This form is called sprouting broccoli. Its developing flower stalk and that of the cabbage are botanically the same thing.

In 1860, at the Royal Agricultural College at Cirencester in southern England, the kale-like wild cabbage from the seacoast was subjected to simple breeding and selection. The forms of broccoli and other related cabbage-like varieties which developed demonstrated their common ancestry.

Like the other forms of *B. oleracea*, the parent type of these cabbages in native to the Mediterranean and Asia Minor. The Romans grew and prized sprouting broccoli, according to Pliny, in the first century after Christ. This is the form still popular in Italy. Despite its antiquity, sprouting broccoli apparently was unknown in England until about 1720, when it was introduced as "sprout cauliflower" or "Italian asparagus." "Green" broccoli (doubtless the sprouting form) was mentioned in an American gardening book in 1806, but it must have been known here long before.

It is surprising that such an excellent vegetable as sprouting broccoli, known for more than 2,000 years in Europe and perhaps 200 years in America, should have become popular here only since about 1920. Americans of Italian origin had grown it for generations in the vicin-

ity of New York and Boston before 1925, when it began to be an important market and home-garden plant in the States. Much of today's crop is quick-frozen.

We occasionally see another sprouting type in this country, called *raab* or *broccoli raab*. An entirely different, low-growing little plant with turnpike foliage, it should not be confused with broccoli of *B. oleracea*.

Cauliflower and cauliflower broccoli have much the same *early* history as sprouting broccoli. The oldest record of cauliflower dates back to the sixth century B.C. Pliny wrote about it in the first century after Christ. In the 12th century three varieties were described in Spain as introductions from Syria, where it had been grown for more than 1,000 years.

European writers mentioned cauliflower in Turkey and Egypt in the 16th century, but it had been known in those places for 1,500 to 2,000 years or more. In England in 1586 cauliflower was referred to as "Cyprus coleworts," suggesting recent introduction from the island of Cyprus. For some time thereafter, Cyprus was mentioned as England's source of seed for planting. Cauliflower was marketed in London as early as 1619. It was grown in France around 1600. A century ago, up to a dozen varieties were listed in American catalogues, as many as are commonly listed today.

Cauliflower and cauliflower broccoli appear alike. In fact, "winter cauliflower" on our markets is cauliflower broccoli, hardier and slower-growing than cauliflower. Most varieties of both require cool, moist air, although heat-tolerant types have been developed in India.

The sensitivity to climate, difficulty of culture, and relatively high price of the cauliflowers have made them true aristocrats of the cabbage family. Some wag has defined cauliflower as "cabbage with a college education."

Sprouting Broccoli (Left) and Cauliflower (Right) Are Edible Flower Parts. Long before heading cabbage was known, the ancient peoples of Mediterranean lands were eating the partially developed flowers and parts of the flower stalks of these "cabbages."

Green Gifts from the Mediterranean

OUR COMMON GARDEN ASPARAGUS (*Asparagus officinalis*) is only one of several edible species of asparagus, but is by far the most important. Our name for it is the Latinized form of the old Greek word, and its European names are similar: *asperge* (French), *Spargel* (German), *asperge* (Dutch), *espárrago* (Spanish).

English and American colloquialisms are sparagrass, sparrowgrass, and among larger growers of the crop, just "grass."

Asparagus is believed native to the eastern Mediterranean lands and Asia Minor. It commonly grows wild there and also in the trans-Caucasus, Europe, and even in places in the United States where it has escaped from cultivation. It thrives along riverbanks, lake shores, even close to sea water, tolerating considerable salt in the soil. It has been found wild in so many places that there has been much argument as to where it actually originated.

Before asparagus was used for food it had quite a reputation as a medicine for almost anything from the prevention of bee stings to heart trouble, dropsy, and toothache!

The Greeks apparently collected asparagus only from the wild. The Romans, however, as early as 200 B.C. gave detailed gardening instructions that might be good today, except that they preferred to use wild seed for planting. Three hundred years later their cultivated forms consistently equaled the best wild plants. In Roman times asparagus was not only eaten "in season" but was dried and later prepared simply by boiling. The Emperor Augustus is supposed to have been very fond of it and to have originated a saying, "Quicker than you can cook asparagus."

North Europeans and Britons have eaten asparagus for as long as their records go back. It was taken to America and other lands by early voyagers, and is now universally popular.

Asparagus (Left) and Endive (Right) Are Ornamental When Grown to Flowering. Native to the Mediterranean and Asia Minor, these food plants were harvested from the wild long before the Romans began to cultivate them. Garden asparagus, once considered a medicine, is distinct from the florists' asparagus "fern."

Asparagus is unusual in its flowering habit. Nearly all our vegetables bear both stamens and pistils (containing pollen cells and egg cells, respectively) on the same plant or flower. In asparagus about half the plants bear only staminate flowers and about half bear only pistillate flowers from which the little red seed-bearing fruits develop. They must be grown near each other to produce seed. The pistillate plants produce fewer but larger and better shoots than the staminate plants.

Asparagus is a perennial plant which, under best conditions, will remain productive up to 30 to 35 years and will live much longer. Formerly it was grown almost entirely with the soil ridged up high over the roots at harvest time so that the shoots would develop in the dark and be white. Now we prefer green shoots which develop in the light, and ridging is no longer so common.

Endive is shown with asparagus in the painting only because it is native to the same general region and, like it, was used as food by the ancients of Mediterranean lands. The two are not at all related botanically. Endive (*Cichorium endivia*) is closely related to chicory, which was introduced as a garden plant, later to become a weed over large areas of the Temperate Zone.

Endive was eaten by the Egyptians and by the Greeks long before the Christian era. The Romans of the first century after Christ also used it, both as a salad and cooked as greens.

Two kinds of endive were grown in northern Europe in the 13th century. Several 16th century writers described the plant in England, France, and Germany. European colonists brought it to America, where in 1806 three varieties were described, similar to those grown today.

Although many dislike the slight bitterness of endive, it is easily grown, is an attractive ingredient of raw-vegetable salads, and is more tolerant to heat than lettuce. It deserves far more popularity than it now enjoys in America.

French endive, or witloof chicory (*Cichorium intybus*), closely related to endive, is little grown as a vegetable in America, but is popular in France and Belgium. The dried, ground, and roasted root of common chicory is used as an adulterant of coffee, even as a substitute for it.

Edible Flower Buds of a Gorgeous Thistle

THE GLOBE ARTICHOKE (*Cynara scolymus*), also called French artichoke and green artichoke, derives its common name from the northern Italian words *articiocco* and *articoclos*. The latter is supposed to involve the Ligurian word *cocali*, meaning a pine cone, to which the Ligurians aptly compared the flower head of the artichoke, a kind of thistle.

Believed to be native to western and central Mediterranean lands, the species was apparently carried to Egypt and farther east some 2,000 to 2,500 years ago. Until comparatively recent times the leaves rather than the flower heads were eaten. To one who is not familiar with this plant, both, when seen full-grown, appear rather coarse and unappetizing.

Another form of this same species is commonly called cardoon (from the Latin *carduus*, meaning thistle). Of this only the young leaves or undeveloped flower stalks are eaten. These parts are grown in darkness so they will be white and tender. It was this form of *Cynara* that ancient Greeks and Romans knew.

The cardoon, or leafy form, was grown about ancient Carthage and in Sicily, Greece, and Italy before the Christian era. It was one of Rome's most popular garden plants in the second century after Christ, bringing a higher price than any other. It was used both as greens (a potherb) and as a salad plant.

This forerunner of the artichoke, like its descendant, resembles an enormous thistle plant. Cardoon has been grown over all the Mediterranean countries for centuries, but was introduced into England as late as 1656 or 1658. It was being grown in America in the 18th century. In parts of Spain an extract of the dried flowers of cardoon was used to curdle milk for making cheese.

The first record of the modern artichoke form, having a flower head and bracts with an edible fleshy basal structure, came from Naples about 1400. From Naples this artichoke was taken to Florence and then to Venice. From Italy it was introduced into England and France.

The artichoke never became nearly so popular in England or in English colonies as in France, Spain, and their colonies. Three varieties were mentioned in the United States in 1806. It is grown here chiefly in Louisiana, settled by the French, and the mid-coastal part of California, settled by the Spanish. The artichoke is considered a luxury here. Its food value is low, yields are relatively small, and it is poorly adapted to most of our country's climate. Market production is mainly in California.

From the early 16th century two main types have been recognized: those with conical flower heads and those nearly globular. The color of the outer parts of the bracts ranges from light green ("white") to purplish ("violet") and reddish purple. Spineless forms are now preferred.

The artichoke will not "come true to seed," as I once learned to my sorrow. Out of several scores that I planted, not one produced a really good head, and they varied widely from the parent plant. The artichoke is grown as a perennial, and good varieties are propagated by sprouts that arise from the crowns in spring. The sprouts grow true to the plant from which they arise.

No flower heads are obtained in the first year of growth. If heads are allowed to develop fully, they produce a showy bloom like that of a thistle but larger. The petals of the myriad flowers that emerge from each head are light purplish or violet. The fleshy base from which these flowers rise is the principal edible part of the immature flower head.

The artichoke belongs to the same family as thistles, sunflowers, lettuce, salsify, chrysanthemums, and thousands of other species. The true artichoke should not be confused with the so-called Jerusalem artichoke—which did not come from Jerusalem and is not an artichoke. The Jerusalem artichoke (*Helianthus tuberosus*) is native to North America, and, as its Latin name indicates, is a tuber-bearing sunflower. A few plants are occasionally grown here for the crisp, small tubers, which are pickled or made into relish.

Our Globe Artichoke Came from a Wild Thistle of Mediterranean Lands. Before the Christian era a gigantic thistle, cardoon, was cultivated for its leaf shoots, which were grown in the dark to make them white and tender. The Italians later developed this artichoke form with fleshy flower parts, eaten when immature.

Celery First Used as a Medicine

CELERY (*Apium graveolens*) is believed to be the same plant as *selinon*, mentioned in Homer's *Odyssey* about 850 B.C. Our word "celery" comes from the French *céleri*, which is derived from the ancient Greek. The old Roman names, as well as many modern ones, derive from the same root word, indicating that its wide distribution and use are rather recent.

Smallage, a plant now grown as a flavoring, is apparently the "wild" celery known in Mediterranean countries for thousands of years. Wild celery grows in wet places over Europe, the Mediterranean lands (where it is thought to have originated), Asia Minor, the Caucasus, and southeast toward the Himalayas. Chinese writings of the fifth century mention it.

The oldest record of the word *céleri* is in a ninth century poem written in France or Italy which gives its medicinal merits. When its garden culture began in 16th century Italy and northern Europe, it was still primitive, like smallage, and used for medicinal purposes only.

Celery's use as food was first recorded in France in 1623, and that as a flavoring only. There and in Italy by the mid-17th century the stalks and leaves were sometimes eaten with an oil dressing. In the late 17th and early 18th centuries in Italy, France, and England the wild type of celery was improved. Gardeners also found they could eliminate much of the too-strong flavor, making the stalks better for salad use, by growing the plants in late summer and

fall, then keeping them into winter. By the mid-18th century, Sweden's wealthier families were enjoying the wintertime luxury of celery that had been stored in cellars. From then on its use as we know it today spread rapidly. We do not know what group of European colonists brought it to America or when, but four cultivated varieties were listed here in 1806.

All through the 19th century in America, England, and much of Europe, it was believed necessary to blanch the green edible portion of celery to rid it of unpleasantly strong flavor and color. This was done by banking the plants with soil. Some kinds, like Pascal and Utah, that remain green when ready for eating are now considered to be of the finest quality.

Many so-called "easy-blanching" or "self-blanching" varieties have appeared in the past 50 years. Generally these are inferior to the best green varieties, but can be grown in less favorable soil and climate.

Celeriac, or turnip-rooted celery, is a kind that forms a solid, greatly enlarged, rather globular body just below the soil surface. Especially suited for soups and stews, it was developed from the same wild species as our present improved celery varieties, and around the same time. Italian and Swiss botanists first described it about 1600. A hundred years later it was becoming a common vegetable in Europe, but it has never been highly popular in England or the United States.

Parsley (*Petroselinum sativum*) belongs to the same family as celery, is native to the same area, and its Latin name reveals a relationship to the old Greek *selinon* mentioned above. In the fourth and third centuries B.C. the Greek word definitely meant parsley. The Latin *Petroselinum* means rock parsley, referring to its habit of growing in rocky places. Unlike celery, parsley has a long and definite ancient history as a food plant. Greeks and Romans knew it well as a flavoring and a garnish, and even used it in festive garlands. Eating it was supposed to ward off intoxication!

Theophrastus described both the crowded, dense-leaved type and the broad, open-growing type in the fourth century B.C. The curled and plain types were common to the Romans in the first century or before and in northern Europe in the 13th century.

Parsley supposedly was introduced into England from Sardinia in 1548, and from Europe to America in the 17th century. Like celery, it produces a "turnip-rooted" form, commonly called Hamburg parsley, used the same as celeriac.

Celery Was Medicine to the Ancients, Parsley a Food. Parsley (right) was cultivated when celery was still wild; Romans ate it to ward off drunkenness. Celery (left) was first used for food only as a flavoring. Large-rooted forms of celery, called celeriac (center), and of parsley are more popular in Europe than in America.

Two Mediterranean Root Crops

THE PARSNIP (*Pastinaca sativa*), like its more popular relative, the carrot, has escaped from cultivation and persisted in the wild. Some reports of its occurring wild have been erroneous, however. Our native water hemlock (*Cicuta*), for example, looks somewhat like the parsnip, but is highly poisonous.

Wild plants resembling parsnips should not be taken for food except by persons skilled in identifying both the poisonous and the non-poisonous kinds.

Parsnips are believed to be native to the eastern Mediterranean area and northeastward, including the Caucasus. The word *pastinaca* of the Romans may have included parsnip along with carrot. In Roman times the parsnip was supposed to have medicinal as well as food value, but we have no proof that either the Greeks or the Romans cultivated it. The Emperor Tiberius supposedly was so fond of parsnips that he had them imported each year from Germany, where they flourished wild along the Rhine. Possibly the Celts of that part of Europe had brought the parsnip back from their forays to the east centuries before.

The modern parsnip was definitely illustrated in Germany in 1542, and again eight years later under the name *Pestnachen*, apparently a Germanized form of the old Roman *pastinaca*. By the mid-16th century it was a staple of Europe's poorer people, as the potato is today.

The 16th century German parsnips were long, like our more popular varieties today. They were doubtless introduced into England no later than the 16th century, since they were well known by the first English colonists in America. They were grown in Virginia in 1609 and were common in Massachusetts 20 years later.

Even the American Indians readily took up parsnip culture. In 1779 Gen. John Sullivan in his forays against the Iroquois in western New York destroyed their stores of parsnips.

The "round" form of parsnip, varying from top-shaped to round, is rarely grown in America. Its origin is unknown, but it was described in France in 1824. The well-known variety called Student was originated a century ago at Cirencester, England, from wild parsnip seed from gardens of the Royal Agricultural College.

The parsnip is a hardy biennial. In spring there arises from each root a tall, much-branched stalk that flowers and produces seeds. These seeds require nearly ideal storage to preserve their vitality for more than a year.

The sweetness of parsnip roots becomes well developed only after they have been exposed to cold, but not necessarily frozen, for a few weeks. The roots, like those of several other hardy vegetables, may be frozen solid without injury if left in the soil until they have thawed.

Salsify (*Tragopogon porrifolius*) is sometimes called oyster plant or vegetable oyster because the flavor of its long, fleshy, white root, when cooked, suggests that of oysters. The name "salsify" is derived from the French *salsifis*. It is also called goatsbeard because of its thin, tufted, grasslike leaves.

This species is distinct from the so-called black salsify, or scorzonera (*Scorzonera hispanica*), and from Spanish salsify, or golden thistle (*Scolymus hispanicus*), neither of which is commonly cultivated in America. Spanish salsify was described by the Greeks and Romans, but they apparently had no interest in the kind we grow. Salsify is both cultivated and found wild in the Mediterranean countries to which it is native. The ancients collected it only from the wild.

T. porrifolius was eaten in Germany and France in the 13th century, but was not grown in gardens at that time. Its cultivation in Europe apparently began around the 16th century. It was grown then in England as an ornamental plant as well as for food.

Since about 1600 salsify has been cultivated widely in Europe, and it was introduced into America before 1800. It grows slowly, is often disappointing in its yield, and is rather exacting in its requirements.

Salsify (Left) and Parsnip (Right) Have Been Cultivated for 2,000 years. Earlier these root crops from the eastern Mediterranean and Asia Minor were gathered wild. Once grown as an ornamental, salsify has a seed head like that of a gigantic dandelion. The parsnip flower and seed head resemble those of celery.

First Beets Yielded Only Greens

SWISS CHARD, garden beets, stock beets, or mangel-wurzels, and sugar beets all belong to the same species (*Beta vulgaris*), a biennial that grows best in a cool climate.

All will intercross readily, the wind-borne pollen fertilizing the pistillate flowers of any plant of the same species. Seed crops of garden beets, for example, must not be grown within several miles of a sugar-beet seed crop lest cross-pollination ruin the purity of seed of both.

Chard, as Americans use the term, applies specifically to the leaf beet (*Beta vulgaris* variety *cicla*), or beet that develops no enlarged, fleshy root. We use the term as a synonym of Swiss chard; "chard," however, also may refer to the succulent blanched petioles of the leaves of the globe artichoke and cardoon (page 132). The Romans called leaf beet *beta*, the Arabs *selg*, and the Portuguese *selga*, apparently an adaptation of the Arabic name.

The wild beet, which occurs widely over Mediterranean lands and the Near East, is believed to have originated in the Mediterranean area, spreading eastward in prehistoric times, with a secondary region of development in the Near East. In ancient times beet leaves were harvested from the wild as a potherb.

Although improved in size, compactness, and edibility over ancient forms, the several types of chard grown now have been known for hundreds, some for thousands of years.

In the fourth century B.C., Aristotle wrote of red chard, and Theophrastus mentioned light-green and dark-green kinds. The Romans knew chard well, but in the Far East it was apparently unknown until the Middle Ages, being mentioned in China only from the seventh century. The lack of a Sanskrit name suggests it was spread from west to east after truly ancient times.

Chard has been used in Europe for as long as there are definite records of food plants there.

Beets and Swiss Chard Are the Same Species; the Romans Knew Both Well. Chard (right) is a primitive, leafy beet that produces no fleshy root. Round beets (left) are the most modern form. The tall, much-branched plant at the left margin has gone to seed.

In the 13th century a German writer used the name *acelga* (*selga* is still used in Spain and Portugal), indicating that it was well established in the Iberian Peninsula. In the 16th century a Swiss botanist described a yellow form, completing the list of types now known.

Beets of the types that produce large, fleshy, edible roots were unknown before the Christian era. The ancients used the root of the wild beet or chard apparently for medicinal purposes only. In the second and third centuries Roman epicures first gave recipes for cooking the root of *Beta vulgaris* (probably a fleshy root selected from wild plants, not the hard, fibrous root of chard), some claiming it was better food than cabbage. The next known record of beet root was in 14th century English recipes.

The red beet with a turniplike root was first described as a food plant in Germany in 1558 and was a rarity at that time in northern Europe. The improved beet was called Roman beet in the 16th century in northern Europe and France, indicating its introduction from Italy. All through the 17th and 18th centuries few kinds of garden beets were known. Up to about 1800 only two kinds, Red and Long Red, were listed by English seedsmen.

In the United States in 1806 only one variety —Red—was listed in a leading catalogue, but in 1828 four kinds were listed. The Basano variety, still grown, was common in Italy more than a century ago. The Flat Egyptian, an American production also cultivated today, was first grown around Boston about 1869. Other varieties grown in America are of more recent introduction.

Colors of garden-beet varieties may range from extremely dark purplish red to bright vermilion all the way to white. The roots of some varieties, when cut transversely, show distinct white and colored rings, like a target.

Beets are commonly grown in home gardens because of their easy culture and quick yield, and tens of thousands of acres are grown annually in this country for canning. During World War II, among all the vegetables dehydrated for military or civilian use, beets were found to be one of the most satisfactory.

Turnip and Its Hybrid Offspring

FOR A LONG TIME much confusion surrounded the origins, even the identity, of turnips and rutabagas. They are distinctly different species. Most varieties of turnip are white-fleshed and most varieties of rutabagas, or Swedes, are yellow-fleshed. (But there are also white-fleshed rutabagas and yellow-fleshed turnips!) Rutabaga leaves are smooth like cabbage leaves, while those of the turnip are somewhat rough, with sparse, stiff "hairs" over them.

The most significant difference between them, however, is in the structures of their individual cells. The turnip has 20 chromosomes, the rutabaga 38. Recent botanical detective work indicates that a rather rare kind of hybridization between some form of cabbage (18 chromosomes) and turnip (20 chromosomes) resulted in the new species, rutabaga (20 + 18 = 38 chromosomes). No one knows when or where this occurred, but the new species was probably first found in Europe in the late Middle Ages. The Swiss botanist Caspar Bauhin described it in 1620.

Turnip (*Brassica rapa*) is of ancient culture; the Romans knew many kinds at the beginning of the Christian era. Some bore Greek place names, indicating earlier culture by the Greeks.

In the first century Pliny described long turnips, flat turnips, and round turnips under the names *rapa* and *napus*. In middle English this latter term became *nepe*, *naep* in Anglo-Saxon. One of these words, together with *turn* ("made round"), became our word "turnip."

Man appreciated the turnip during agriculture's prehistoric development. So easy to grow in so many places, it became distributed from the Mediterranean across Asia to the Pacific.

The European types of turnip, our commonest kinds, developed in the Mediterranean area and were used in France for both food and stock feed at least as early as the first century after Christ. The basic center for Asiatic kinds is in middle Asia, west of the Himalayas. Two secondary centers are eastern Asia and Asia Minor.

In the England of Henry VIII, turnip roots were boiled or baked, the tops were cooked as greens, and the young shoots were used as a salad. (In parts of our South today turnip leaves for greens are called "turnip salad.")

Jacques Cartier brought the turnip to Canada in 1541. It was also planted in Virginia by the colonists in 1609 and in Massachusetts in the 1620's; the Indians soon adopted its culture. It has since been one of the commonest cool-weather garden vegetables in America.

European varieties of turnips are biennial. One Oriental variety commonly grown here, however, called Shogoin, will go to seed in its first season if planted in the spring.

A few varieties of leaf turnips (no enlarged root) such as Seven Top are grown only for greens. Turnip leaves are usually rich in minerals and vitamins, but the roots have a relatively low food value. In this country the roots, either fresh or from pit or cellar storage, are usually eaten boiled. In Europe kraut is commonly made from sliced roots.

Rutabaga (*Brassica napobrassica*) gets its name from Swedish *rotabagge*. In England and Canada it is commonly called Swede, or Swede turnip. The French called it *navet de Suède* (Swede turnip), *chou de Suède* (Swede cabbage), and *chou navet jaune* (yellow cabbage turnip). It was known in the United States about 1800 as "turnip-rooted cabbage." Although common names suggest a Scandinavian origin, this is not certain.

Rutabaga was apparently known on the Continent many years before it was grown in England's royal gardens in 1664. It was eaten in France and southern Europe in the 17th century. Both white- and yellow-fleshed varieties have been known there for more than 300 years.

The rutabaga requires a longer growing season than our turnips, but is similarly sensitive to hot weather. Its culture is confined largely to the northernmost States and Canada and to northern Europe and Asia. More nutritious than the turnip, it is a staple in northern Europe, but a minor crop in America and in the Orient.

The Turnip (Right) Is Older than History; the Rutabaga (Left) Is Almost Modern. From their original home in western Asia and the eastern Mediterranean, turnips spread over most of Asia before recorded history. The more nutritious rutabaga, or Swede, is a cabbage-turnip hybrid that appeared in the late Middle Ages.

Near Eastern Plant in American Pies

RHUBARB'S ECONOMIC and dietary importance in America is limited, but it is rather unusual among our common vegetables and there is widespread interest in growing it.

Our word "rhubarb" comes from the French *rhubarbe*, a contraction of the Late Latin *rheubarbarum*, which refers to a rhubarb species called *rheum barbarum*. In America rhubarb is also called pieplant because of its common use in pies.

About a dozen so-called species of rhubarb have been described from various regions in Eurasia, but we know little about their relationships or origins. Our most popular varieties belong to the species *Rheum rhaponticum*, which is believed native to the eastern Mediterranean and Asia Minor. Other edible species are found wild in middle Asia and in China. The earliest records of the use of rhubarb date from about 2700 B.C., in China, where the root was—and still is—used for medicinal purposes.

Only the fleshy leaf stalks, the enormous petioles, of the rhubarb are edible. The root contains potent substances that would cause violent digestive disturbances, and the leaf blades or leaves sometimes contain enough harmful substances to cause serious illness or even death, if eaten.

Rhubarb of the garden type was introduced into Europe from the East relatively late. It was cultivated at Padua, Italy, about 1608, and some 25 to 30 years later seeds of it were obtained for planting in England. In the early 1700's there were several references to its culture in Europe and England, but not until 1778 was it definitely recorded as a food plant there, used for making tarts and pies.

A gardener in Maine apparently got rhubarb from Europe about 1790 to 1800 and introduced it to market gardeners in Massachusetts. By 1806 it was used in New England tarts and pies,

but not extensively. By 1822 it was generally grown and marketed in Massachusetts; it was listed in an American seed catalogue in 1828.

Various rhubarbs were introduced into Europe and England in the late 18th and early 19th centuries from China and India.

One record of 1861 described how the Afghans near Kabul blanched the leaf stalks of a wild species of rhubarb by piling as much as one and one-half feet of loose gravel over the sprouts when they emerged. Sometimes earthen jars were inverted over the plants, forcing the stalks to grow white and crookedly.

Victoria and Linnaeus have been the commonest varieties of rhubarb for generations. They are both large, productive kinds having leaf stalks that are light green or tinged and streaked with crimson. In recent years attractive, definitely crimson or "red" varieties, like Ruby and MacDonald, have been in demand.

Rhubarb is a cool-climate perennial, requiring a good winter rest to thrive year after year. In North America it grows to perfection in the northernmost States and in southern Canada. Under favorable conditions some varieties will produce almost incredibly large plants with leaf stalks up to three feet long and as thick as a boy's wrist. The leaf blades grow up to two and one-half feet across. Gardeners usually cut out the tall-growing seed stalks when they appear in spring, because seed production is believed to hinder the best growth of leaf stalks.

Rhubarb does not come true to seed; to keep varieties "pure" one must propagate them vegetatively, by dividing the clumps of plants. A "piece" of rhubarb plant for planting in the garden must contain some of the large fleshy root together with some of the compact underground stem structure and buds from which the leaves arise. It takes about three years to reach a fairly productive stage.

A few gardeners grow fields of rhubarb for forcing. After the plants have become large and sturdy in the field, the entire underground parts are taken in late winter or very early spring before growth starts and planted in special heated, dimly lighted houses. There leaf stalks grow rapidly and attain fine quality.

Rhubarb Came to Our Gardens from the Eastern Mediterranean and Asia Minor. The rhubarb, or "pieplant," of American gardens differs from the Chinese rhubarb grown for its medicinal root. Rhubarb is a perennial requiring a cool winter's rest to thrive. Its leaves should never be eaten; they are sometimes poisonous.

An African Native of World Popularity

THE WATERMELON (*Citrullus vulgaris*) is hardly a vegetable, but it is such a universally popular truck or garden crop that it has a place here.

The culture of the watermelon goes back to prehistoric times. It was grown by the ancient Egyptians, surviving pictures reveal. Old names in Arabic, Berber, Sanskrit, Spanish, and Sardinian are all unrelated, indicating its great antiquity in lands about the Mediterranean and east as far as India.

Watermelons have been grown to an important extent in the warmer parts of Russia, the Near East, and Middle East for thousands of years, but reached China apparently only about a thousand years ago.

The long and general culture of the watermelon from North Africa to middle Asia led to the view that it was of Asiatic origin, although it had never been found wild. Finally, however, about a hundred years ago, the great missionary-explorer, David Livingstone, settled the question of its origin. He found large tracts in central Africa literally covered with watermelons growing truly wild.

In the wild state both bitter and sweet melons occur in the same locality, but the bitter ones appear no different from the sweet. The natives therefore knock a hole in each fruit to taste the juice before taking it for food or drink. In certain semidesert districts in Africa the natives cultivate the watermelon as an important source of water during dry periods.

The plant was doubtless known many hundreds of years ago in all European countries where it could be grown. European botanists of the 16th and 17th centuries described all the sizes and shapes, rind, seed, and flesh colors that we now know. These include yellow and white flesh as well as red; and white, red, brown, black, green, and speckled seeds.

Watermelon, Africa's Greatest Contribution to the Joy of Eating. This plump, juicy favorite, a boon in water-short regions, still grows wild in its native African heartland. Cultivated since antiquity, it is grown in "hills" about eight feet apart, two or three plants to a hill. Georgia leads in United States production.

The watermelon was brought to America by some of the earliest European colonists, being common in Massachusetts in 1629. The Florida Indians were said to have been growing watermelons by the mid-1600's, and Father Marquette, French explorer of the Mississippi, mentioned them in 1673 as being grown in the interior of the country.

In America the watermelon is used almost entirely as a dessert, to be eaten fresh—and cold. The rind, however, is sometimes made into preserves or sweet pickles. The seeds are used in this country only for planting.

An old report stated that in southern Russia a beer was made from watermelon juice. The juice may be boiled down to a heavy syrup like molasses for its sugar.

In Iraq, and in Egypt and elsewhere in Africa, the flesh of the melon is used as a staple food and animal feed as well as a source of water in some dry districts. In the Old World, particularly Asia, the seeds are roasted, with or without salting, and eaten from the hand. Orientals also preserve watermelon by salting or brining large pieces or halves in barrels.

Although melons weighing 25 to 40 pounds are most popular in America, our seed catalogues have listed small varieties such as Baby Delight, Northern Sweet, and Sweet Siberian for many years. These small five- to ten-pound melons have long been grown in cooler areas where the summers are short. Greatly oversized watermelons have no sound market value. They are difficult to handle without damage or wastage, most customers do not want them, and they are often inferior to those of normal size.

Although the watermelon will *not* cross with pumpkin, squash, or cucumber, it will cross with the so-called preserving melon, or citron, which is simply a hard, white-fleshed watermelon, good only for making preserves. Cross-pollination with citron causes no harm unless the seed of fruit from a cross-pollinated flower is planted. Such seed produces mixed, poor quality melons.

"Seedless" watermelons have been produced experimentally in recent years by two wholly different methods, but neither seems practical as yet for use by farmers and gardeners.

Okra, or Gumbo, from Africa

OKRA (*Hibiscus esculentus*) is also called gumbo in this country, although the latter term is more often applied to soups or other dishes which contain okra. Both of these names are of African origin. "Gumbo" is believed to be a corruption of a Portuguese corruption, *quingombo*, of the word *quillobo*, native name for the plant in the Congo and Angola area of Africa.

Okra originated, according to one study, in the Abyssinian center of origin of cultivated plants, an area that includes present-day Ethiopia, the plateau portion of Eritrea, and the eastern, higher part of the Sudan. Considering the relative isolation of this region and the antiquity of the trail, it is not surprising that little definite is known about the origin and prehistoric distribution of okra.

The routes by which okra was taken from Ethiopia to North Africa, the eastern Mediterranean, Arabia, and southeast Asia, and when, are by no means certain. Although it has been commonly cultivated in Egypt for many hundreds of years, no sign of it has ever been found in any monument or relic of ancient Egypt.

Since the Spanish Moors and the Egyptians of the 12th and 13th centuries used an Arab word for okra, it probably was taken into Egypt by Moslems from the East who conquered Egypt in the seventh century. It requires no stretch of the imagination to suppose that the plant much earlier was taken from Ethiopia to Arabia across the narrow Red Sea or the narrower strait at its southern end.

From Arabia okra was spread over North Africa, completely around the Mediterranean, and eastward. The absence of any ancient Indian names for it is puzzling, in view of its evident antiquity in southeast Asia.

Although the plant has been well known in India for a long time, it is not found wild there. Modern travelers have found okra growing truly wild, however, in the upper Nile country as well as in Ethiopia.

One of the earliest accounts of okra is by a Spanish Moor who visited Egypt in 1216. He described the plant in detail, as cultivated by the Egyptians, and stated that the pods when young and tender were eaten with meal.

Because of the outstanding popularity of okra in the French cookery of Louisiana, and its slow gain in popularity elsewhere in this country, it is safe to assume that it was introduced here by the French colonists of Louisiana in the early 1700's. It had been brought to the New World, however, before 1658, reaching Brazil supposedly from Africa. It was known in Surinam in 1686.

Strangely, records of okra during early American colonial times are lacking, although it must have been common among French colonists. It was being grown as far north as Philadelphia in 1748; Jefferson said it was known in Virginia before 1781, and from about 1800 onward numerous garden writers mentioned it. Several distinct varieties were known in 1806.

Many people fail to appreciate okra because they do not know how to use it. The fast-growing pods must be harvested frequently, when only three to five days old. In hot weather they may become too old and tough for use less than a week after developing from the pollinated flower. Also, because of its rather "gooey," mucilaginous, quality, okra is rarely used alone in America, except when sliced, dipped in corn meal, and fried. Usually just a little of it is cooked with other vegetables, or in soups and stews. However, thousands of tons of the pods are grown in the South for soup companies.

In some lands the seeds rather than the whole young pods are of most interest. When ripe the seeds yield an edible oil, commonly used in Mediterranean countries and the East, that is the equal of many other cooking oils.

The ripe seeds of okra are sometimes roasted and ground as a substitute for coffee. A close relative, roselle, is a source of fiber for cloth. In Turkey, leaves are used in preparing a medicament to soothe inflammation.

Okra, Related to Cotton, Began Its Journeys from the Abyssinian Plateau. In prehistoric times okra was carried from Ethiopia to Arabia and eastward, also down the Nile; thence by the Moors to Europe and probably by the French to America. Fast-growing pods, best when only three or four days old, are easily dried for later use

Universal Boon to the Salad Bowl

LETTUCE (*Lactuca sativa*) is the world's most popular salad plant. Both its common and its Latin name are based on its heavy, milky juice. The word "lettuce" is probably derived from the Old French *laitues* (plural of *laitue*), meaning milky, referring to this plant. The Latin root word *lac* (milk) appears in the Latin name *lactuca*. Ancient Greeks called lettuce *tridax*; the old Persians, *kahn*.

Cultivated lettuce is closely related to the wild lettuce, *L. scariola*, from which it derived. Wild lettuce is now widely scattered over the globe, but it originated in inner Asia Minor, the trans-Caucasus, Iran, and Turkistan.

According to Herodotus, lettuce was served on the tables of Persian kings of the sixth century B.C, In the fifth and fourth centuries B.C., other Greek writers praised its virtues. It was popular among the Romans about the beginning of the Christian era; writers of that period described a dozen sorts in cultivation.

Common garden lettuce (*L. sativa*) was known in China in the fifth century, if not earlier. In addition, a form of "stem lettuce" is native to China. The so-called asparagus lettuce and others of this type with long, narrow leaves and tall, thick, edible stems are grown in America only as curiosities.

The primitive forms of lettuce, like those of the cabbages, were loose, leafy, and sometimes "stemmy" types; the loose-heading and firm-heading forms occurred much later.

Cos lettuce (romaine) forms an erect, compact rosette of elongated leaves, approaching the character of a head. It is relatively tolerant to heat and evidently developed in a moderately warm climate. The old records and its name indicate an Italian origin. Common in Italy in the Middle Ages, the type is said to have been taken to France from Italy in 1537 by Rabelais. In the late 16th century it was still rare in France and Germany. Undeservedly, it is grown today only to a minor extent in our home gardens.

Firm-heading forms had become well developed in Europe by the 16th century, but when they first were developed is unknown. The oak-leaved and curled-leaf types, and various colors now known, were all described in the 16th and 17th centuries in Europe. Light-green, dark-green, and red-spotted forms of romaine, for example, were described in 1623.

Columbus evidently carried lettuce to the New World, for its culture was reported on Isabela Island (now called Crooked Island) in the Bahamas in 1494. It was common in Haiti in 1565, and evidently was introduced into South America soon after the discovery. It was under cultivation in Brazil before 1650. Lettuce was probably among the first garden seeds sown in every European colony on this continent.

Loose-leaf lettuces are still popular for home gardens because they are so easy to grow, but this highly perishable form is rarely grown for sale except in greenhouses.

Most of our present commercial lettuce is of one strain or another of the Great Lakes variety or of the several Imperial strains. Although they differ in adaptability and behavior in the field, these varieties and strains appear much alike. They are erroneously called Iceberg lettuce. Iceberg is a red-tinged variety of no commercial importance.

The development of these Imperial and related strains of lettuce is one of the outstanding plant-breeding achievements of modern times. They were developed to resist mildew and brown blight, diseases that were rapidly wrecking the lettuce industry of the Southwest back about 1920. Now nearly all lettuce grown there is of these resistant strains. Generally they are not well adapted to the East or South.

Lettuce is an annual plant that requires a relatively cool climate for good leaf and head growth. Hot weather causes it to become bitter and hastens the elongation of its stem into a tall seed stalk, either preventing heading (in head varieties) or causing them to be loose and of poor quality. Head lettuce is exacting in its climate, soil, and cultural requirements.

Lettuce, the World's Most Popular Salad Plant, Hails from the Near East. Loose-leaf lettuce (lower right) is the most primitive cultivated kind. Romaine (middle right) gets its name from its Roman origin. Hard-heading kinds (left) appeared during the Middle Ages in Europe.

Muskmelons Originated in Persia

THE MUSKMELON (*Cucumis melo*), like the water-melon, is hardly a vegetable, but it is an important truck and garden crop. There is a confusing tendency in America to refer to both merely as "melons."

The most popular type of muskmelon that we grow in America is the small, oval, heavily netted kind commonly called cantaloupe. All cantaloupes are muskmelons, but not all muskmelons are cantaloupes.

Muskmelons have a wide range of other forms, sizes, and flesh qualities, such as the Honey Dew, Casaba, and Persian types. The large Bender, Montreal, and such odd varieties as the elongated Banana should not be called cantaloupes. Varieties of muskmelon will inter-cross freely, but will not cross with watermelon, cucumber, pumpkin, or squash.

Muskmelon is so named because of the delightful odor of the ripe fruits. *Musk* is a Persian word for a kind of perfume; *melon* is French, from the Latin *melopepo*, meaning "apple-shaped melon" and derived from Greek words of similar meaning.

Muskmelon is native to Persia (Iran) and adjacent areas, west and east. Persia and Transcaucasia are believed to be the main center of origin and development, with a secondary center including the northwest provinces of India, also Kashmir and Afghanistan. Although truly wild forms of *C. melo* have not been found, several related wild species have been noted in those

regions. The oldest supposed record of the plant is Egyptian, around 2400 B.C. In an illustration of funerary offerings appears a fruit some experts believe to be muskmelon.

The Greeks appear to have known the fruit in the third century B.C., and in the first century after Christ it was definitely described by the Roman naturalist, Pliny, who said it was something new in Campania. The Greek physician, Galen, in the second century wrote of its medicinal qualities, and Roman writers of the following century gave directions for growing it and preparing it with spices for eating. The Chinese apparently did not know the muskmelon until its introduction from west of the Himalayas around the start of the Christian era.

Culture of the muskmelon spread westward over the Mediterranean area in the Middle Ages and apparently was common in Spain by the 15th century. Columbus carried its seeds on his second voyage and had them planted on Isabela Island in 1494, doubtless its first culture in the New World. About this same time Charles VIII of France reputedly introduced muskmelons into central and northern Europe from Rome.

The frequent occurrence of poor flavor in the fruit no doubt explains why its culture spread no more rapidly than it did. As a Spanish writer of 1513 observed: ' If it is bad, it is a bad thing, we are wont to say that the good are like good women, and the bad like bad women."

By the late 16th century, the Spaniards probably had introduced the plant to many places in North America. It was grown in the first English colonies in Virginia and Massachusetts. In the mid-1600's the Indians of Florida, the Middle West, and New England commonly grew it, as their cousins of tropical America had learned to do from the Spaniards a century earlier.

The muskmelon is reported to have been introduced into Bermuda in 1609 and by the Spaniards into California in 1683. It was grown in Brazil before 1650.

The principal types and various sizes, shapes, and colors now grown were known in the 16th century. That does not mean, of course, that our present varieties date back that far, only that their main characteristics were also known in those days. Improvements have been made in uniformity within varieties, in size and shape of fruits, and especially in thickness and quality of flesh. Practically all cantaloupes now grown in California's Imperial Valley, one of the greatest melon-producing districts in the country, are of special strains recently developed to resist the disease called powdery mildew.

Ancient Persians Savored the Muskmelon, Native to Iran and Near-by Lands. Kinds familiar today include, left to right, the long Banana variety, Santa Claus, large Montreal, cantaloupe, and Honey Dew—all muskmelons of Persian lineage. To early Greeks, muskmelon had medicinal properties; Romans ate it with spices.

Carrots for Valuable Vitamin A

THE CARROT (*Daucus carota*) gets its name from the French word *carotte*, which in turn comes from the Latin *carota*. It has been known since ancient times and is believed to have originated in Afghanistan and adjacent areas.

A wide diversity of forms unknown in America is found in middle Asia and also in Asia Minor. Apparently some primitive forms were carried to Asia Minor far back in prehistoric times, and many distinct kinds were later developed there. Among the kinds strange to us in America are some with purplish-red roots, colored like garden beets, and some with fuzzy light-gray leaves.

Our common carrot is called the Mediterranean type, because it has long been known in that region and was probably developed there from kinds carried from Asia Minor. In the Far East is still another form, the Japanese carrot, commonly three feet long or more.

As is true of a number of other vegetables, it seems that the first interest in carrots as food developed from their supposed medicinal value. Greek agriculturists and physicians around the first century of our era wrote of their value as a stomach tonic.

Significantly, in America in the past 30 to 40 years the humble carrot has risen from an obscure root, considered mainly as a delicacy for horses, to a position of genuine importance in our diet. Doctors and nutrition experts have taught us that carrots are "good for us"; we know that varieties with a deep orange color are rich in carotene, or provitamin A, present also in other yellow vegetables and in green leaves. (Vitamin A is found in such foods of animal origin as fish-liver oils, butter, and egg yolks.)

The carrot was certainly cultivated in the Mediterranean area before the Christian era, but it was not important as a food until much later. A gap of about 900 years separates Greek and Roman writings of the first to third centuries and the next clear records about the carrot. By the 13th century carrots were being grown in fields, orchards, gardens, and vineyards in Germany and France. At that time the plant was known also in China, where it was supposed to have come from Persia. By the 16th century, Europe's botanists and writers on gardening were describing many kinds, including red and purple kinds in France, yellow and red kinds in England. About 1600, in England, carrots were grown as a farm crop as well as in gardens.

European voyagers carried the carrot to America soon after discovery of the New World, as is shown by Sir John Hawkins's reference to it on Margarita Island, off the coast of Venezuela, in 1565. It was grown by the struggling colonists of the first permanent English settlement in the New World, at Jamestown, Virginia, in 1609. Twenty years later the Pilgrims, or some of those who followed them closely, were growing it in Massachusetts. Before the middle of the 17th century it was known in Brazil.

Even the American Indians rather promptly took up carrot culture. In forays against the Iroquois in upper New York State in 1779 Gen. John Sullivan's forces destroyed stores of carrots as well as parsnips. In the Northwest, children of the Flathead tribe are said to have liked carrots so well that they could not resist stealing them from the fields.

The carrots having spherical roots and tapering roots have long been known, but the cylindrical stump-rooted sorts were first grown in America about 60 years ago.

All varieties of importance in this country are deep orange in color, although yellow and even white kinds are known. Some of the deep-colored varieties are erroneously referred to as "red." This error has even crept into the name of a currently popular variety, Red Cored Chantenay, which is a rich orange color, not red. It is interesting, however, that pure carotene, which makes carrots yellow or orange, appears red.

In addition to the large quantities marketed fresh, we find carrots canned and frozen, especially in a mixture with green garden peas.

Vitamin-conscious Americans Now Eat Carrots for Health as Well as Taste. Ancient Greeks believed the carrot, grown in the Near East since time immemorial, to have beneficial effect; modern science explains it. The orange color in these round, top-shaped, "half-long," or long roots comes from carotene, a source of vitamin A.

Onions and Other Pungent Lilies

THE BULBOUS ONION and its many relatives belong to the Lily family. Some of these alliums are distinctly ornamental. Others, notably garlic, leek, Welsh onion, and chive, are common vegetables with related flavors and odors due principally to a volatile, irritating substance.

Our word "onion" comes from the Middle English *unyun*, from the French *oignon*, which came in turn from the Latin *unio*, meaning onion. The plant's ancient names in Sanskrit, Hebrew, Greek, and Latin appear unrelated, indicating widespread culture of onions from prehistoric times.

The common onion (*Allium cepa*), leek, and garlic originated in middle Asia, with secondary centers of development and distribution in western Asia and Mediterranean lands. The Welsh onion is believed of Chinese origin; its name is a corruption of the German *walsch*, meaning foreign, and has no reference to Wales.

The ancient Egyptians used onions extensively, as shown by drawings and inscriptions. The Bible states how, during the wanderings of the Israelites in the wilderness, they longed for the onions, leeks, and garlic they had had in Egypt. In the first century many onion varieties were known: long, round, red, yellow, white, strong, and mild kinds. For a time in the Middle Ages the onion seemed less popular than leek and garlic; now the reverse is true.

The Spanish introduced the onion into the West Indies soon after their discovery. From there it soon spread to all parts of the Americas. Onions were grown by the earliest colonists and soon afterward by the Indians.

The Welsh onion (*A. fistulosum*) never forms a rounded bulb—only long white scallions. This form is most popular in the Orient, but is grown almost everywhere. In Japan it is often incorrectly called Japanese leek.

The so-called Egyptian tree onion, or top onion, produces "sets" (tiny bulbs) at the top of the stalk instead of flowers and seeds.

The leek (*A. porrum*), like the Welsh onion, forms only a cylindrical bulb. The leaf of the leek, however, is flattened and solid, while the leaf of the onion is cylindrical and hollow.

Our word "leek" comes from the Anglo-Saxon *leac*. The Romans called it *porrum*, and considered that the best leeks came from Egypt, where they had been known in earliest Biblical times. The Emperor Nero reportedly was nicknamed Porrophagus because of his inordinate appetite for leeks. He imagined they improved his voice! In the sixth century the Welsh attributed a victory over the Saxons to the leeks they wore to identify themselves in battle.

Leeks have been common all over Europe for as long as we have records of food plants. In America, by 1775, they were cultivated by the Indians as well as the colonists.

Garlic (*A. sativum*) has a long history like that of the onion and leek. Its name comes from the Anglo-Saxon *garleac* (*gar*, meaning spear or lance, and *leac* meaning leek). Homer wrote of it in the ninth century B.C.

The Romans disliked the strong flavor and odor of garlic but fed it to their laborers to make them strong and to their soldiers to make them courageous. It is supposed to have been introduced into China in the first or second century B.C., and references to it there occur from the 15th century onward. Europeans have used it commonly for 2,000 years and more.

Garlic's first mention in America is that Cortés fed on it in Mexico, though the Spanish must have introduced it into the West Indies or Central America earlier. The Indians liked it best of all root or bulb crops from Europe.

Chive (*A. schoenoprasum*) is an Old World plant now found wild in Italy and Greece. It is believed native to the eastern Mediterranean. The name is an Old French form of the French *cive*, derived from the Latin *cepa*, meaning onion. Chive has been grown for centuries in Europe. Its attractive blue flowers often produce no seed. It can be propagated from bulbs, which increase in number each year, forming dense clumps.

Onions and Their Kin Put Zest in the Foods of Biblical Times. Israelites, after fleeing from Egypt, pined for them in the wilderness. Large onions and small chives (left), dry garlic and green leek (right) differ in pungency and flavor. All have an odor characteristic of that part of the Lily family they represent, the genus *Allium*.

Garden Peas and Spinach from the Middle East

THE PEA (*Pisum sativum*) gets its English name indirectly from the Latin *pisum*, which resembles the older Greek *pisos*, or *pison*. In Anglo-Saxon the word became *pise* or *pisu*; later, in English it was "pease." So many people thought pease was plural that they persisted in dropping the "s" sound, thus making the word "pea."

Many different species have been called pea, so this word alone is not definite. In our own South today "peas" usually means some edible variety of cowpeas. In referring to what the rest of the United States understands as "peas" (*P. sativum*), the southerner says "English peas."

The main center of origin and development of this pea is middle Asia, from northwest India through Afghanistan and adjacent areas. A second area of development lies in the Near East, and a third includes Ethiopia. In these areas wild peas of related species have been found, along with many cultivated forms of *P. sativum*, but wild *P. sativum* has never been discovered.

Seeds of primitive peas have been found in mud where Swiss lake dwellers lived some 5,000 years ago. Peas perhaps even older were found buried in a cave in Hungary. Despite recurrent claims, this species of pea has not been found among ancient Egyptian treasures, but it has been found on the site of Troy. Aryans from the East are supposed to have introduced peas to the pre-Christian Greeks and Romans.

The pea was first grown only for its dry seed. Some varieties are grown today for dry seeds for split-pea soup, but the varieties known until about 1,000 years ago had much smaller and darker colored seeds than our garden types.

There is no hint of "green peas" until after the Norman Conquest of England. In the 12th century "green peas for Lent" were mentioned, but nothing definite was recorded about them until 1536, when they were described in France. The edible-podded pea was also known then.

Before the end of the 16th century, botanists in Belgium, Germany, and England described many kinds of peas—tall and dwarf, with white, yellow, green seed colors; smooth, pitted, and wrinkled seeds. But in 17th century France they were still such a rare delicacy that fantastic prices were sometimes paid for them.

"This subject of peas continues to absorb all others," wrote Madame de Maintenon in 1696. "Some ladies, even after having supped at the Royal Table, and well supped too, returning to their own homes, at the risk of suffering from indigestion, will again eat peas before going to bed. It is both a fashion and a madness."

The English developed fine varieties; hence the common designation "English peas" in America. About a century ago the famous Austrian monk, Gregor Johann Mendel, worked with peas in founding the science of genetics.

Spinach (*Spinacia oleracea*) has remarkably similar-sounding names in the languages of many widely separated lands, indicating a rather recent spread to those lands. Our name for spinach comes from the Old French *espinache*, which was derived from similar-sounding Arabic or Persian words. The Armenian name is *spanax* and the Spanish is *spanacha*, or *espinaca*. The technical Latinized name *spinacia* was devised probably not before the 12th or 13th century.

Spinach is native to Iran (Persia) and adjacent areas. It apparently was unknown elsewhere until about the beginning of the Christian era. Even then it was unknown to the Greeks and Romans. The earliest record of spinach is in China, where it was introduced from Nepal A.D. 647. Old writings indicate that it reached Spain about A.D. 1100, brought from North Africa by the Moors, who probably got it by way of Syria and Arabia.

The prickly seeded form of spinach (still grown) was known in 13th century Germany and by the 14th century it was commonly grown in European monastery gardens. A cookbook of 1390 for Richard II's court contained recipes for *spynoches*. Smooth-seeded spinach was described in 1522. Spinach doubtless first arrived in America in early colonial times.

Peas Were Introduced in Europe in the Stone Age; Spinach Came Much Later. Both were native to the Near and Middle East. Greeks and Romans grew peas for dry seeds, but held them in no special favor. Green garden peas were uncommon until the 18th century. Spinach was unknown beyond its homeland until 2,000 years ago.

Pickles and Salads Owe a Debt to India

INDIA HAS GIVEN THE WORLD many important food and other crop plants, but only four vegetables are among them. One is the cucumber (*Cucumis sativus*). The others are eggplant, Indian mustard, and cowpeas.

The English word "cucumber" comes from the Latin name *cucumis*. The Bohemian *agurka*, German *Gurke*, Greek *aggouria*, and our word "gherkin," meaning a small cucumber pickle, all trace back to an old Aryan word. Sometimes we facetiously refer to this vegetable as "cowcum-

ber," not realizing that English writers called it that in all seriousness 300 years ago.

The cucumber is believed native to the great Indian center of plant origins between the northern part of the Bay of Bengal and the towering Himalayas. It has never been found wild anywhere, but closely related species grow wild in that region of India.

The profusion of ancient names for it in Aryan, Greek, Latin, Arabic, Armenian, and other tongues indicates that the cucumber was carried westward from India long before written history. The ancient Egyptians may have grown it, but there is no scientific proof that they did.

One old record claims that the cucumber was introduced into China as recently as the second century B.C. Early in the Christian era it was

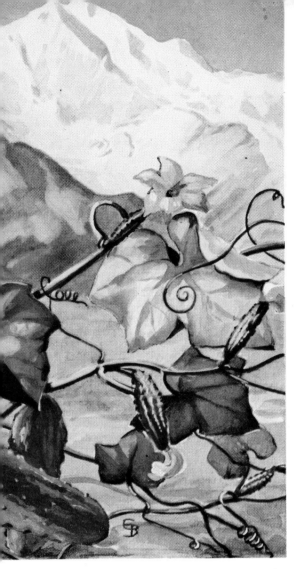

grown in North Africa as well as in Italy, Greece, Asia Minor, and countries to the east.

The Romans used highly artificial methods to grow cucumbers out of season for the Emperor Tiberius; he reportedly ate them every day of the year. They grew in Charlemagne's gardens in ninth century France. England knew them in the early 1300's, but the art of growing them was apparently lost there through a long period of war and turmoil. They were re-introduced from the continent some 250 years later.

Columbus brought the cucumber to the New World, with many other vegetables. He had them planted in Haiti in 1494, and possibly on other islands. Reports of finding the Indians in Canada growing cucumbers in 1535 seem hardly probable so soon after Columbus introduced

them to the West Indies; the plants seen may actually have been some form of native squash or gourd. Reports that in 1539 De Soto found the Indians of Florida growing cucumbers "better than those of Spain" are more credible.

Explorers who touched Virginia in 1584 mentioned cucumbers. Presumably Indians spread them after the Spaniards introduced them far to the south. They were grown in the first permanent English settlements, in Virginia in 1609 and in Massachusetts in 1629. Before the American Revolution eastern Indian tribes and colonists were growing cucumbers generally. They were grown in Brazil before 1650.

Most of the distinct types of cucumber grown today were known at least 400 years ago. Present forms range from thick, stubby little fruits, three to four inches long, up to the great English greenhouse varieties often nearly two feet long. The most popular European and American varieties now have smooth, dark-green skin. Some Russian varieties are short and thick, with a rough, netted brown skin. Large white varieties of a thick, irregular shape, grown in 19th century France for use in cosmetics, supposedly reached northern Europe from Spain.

The enormous English "forcing" (greenhouse) type of cucumber, as marketed, is almost completely seedless. Its fruits, unlike those of varieties commonly grown in America, will develop without any pollination of the pistillate flowers, and therefore without forming seeds.

How does the grower obtain seeds for planting? He pollinates the flowers by hand, or puts bees into the greenhouse to do the job for him.

The so-called "gherkins" that we buy pickled are simply small cucumbers. The true or West Indian gherkin is a different species (*C. anguria*) rarely grown here. It produces a warty (or "prickly") oval fruit about an inch long.

159

Eggplant and Indian Mustard, Two More Asiatics

EGGPLANT (*Solanum melongena*) is so called because the first varieties known to English-speaking people bore colorful egg-shaped fruits.

Spaniards of the 16th century called eggplants *berengenas*, or "apples of love," while some northern European botanists of the same period called the species *Mala insana*, or "mad apple," because they thought eating it would cause insanity. Equally unfounded was the idea in medieval Europe that it possessed remarkable properties as a love potion.

Eggplant is believed to have originated in the Indian center of plant origins, which includes Assam and Burma. Many different names for it in ancient Sanskrit, Bengali, and Hindustani indicate its antiquity in India. Distinctly different, small-fruited kinds developed in a secondary center in China.

Although cultivated in Asia from remote prehistory, eggplant appears to have been known to the Western world no more than about 1,500 years. Numerous Arabic and North African names for it, and the lack of ancient Greek and Roman names, indicate that it was carried into the Mediterranean area by the Arabs in the early Middle Ages. *Melongena*, now part of the scientific name, was a 16th century Arabic name for one kind of eggplant.

One of the oldest records about eggplant is in a fifth century Chinese book; next oldest are from Arabia in the 9th, 10th, and 12th centuries. The Moors carried eggplant west as far as Spain,

where it was known in the 12th century or earlier. In northern Europe it was first mentioned by Albert of Cologne in the 13th century, but was not well known until the mid-16th century.

Yellow and purple varieties were introduced into Germany from Naples about 1550. Fifty years later, white, ash-colored, and brown varieties were also known in Germany, including round, oblong, pear-shaped, and long-fruited kinds.

Travelers to India in the 18th century described all of these and also the green-fruited and variegated varieties grown there. In 16th century Europe varieties were known both with and without spines on the stems, leaves, and calyxes of the fruits.

Introduced early into America by the Spaniards, it was grown in Brazil before 1650. In the United States purple and white varieties for ornament were described in 1806. Until a mere 50 years ago many varieties of eggplant grown in America were for ornament only.

In this country today we grow only the large purple sorts, but people of other lands, especially in the Orient, prefer varieties with small elongated fruits that can be fried or otherwise cooked whole. In Japan eggplant is the third or fourth most important vegetable (after sweet potato, radish, and perhaps Chinese cabbage).

Indian mustard (*Brassica juncea*) in this country is usually called merely "mustard." Most of our large-leaved, fancy, pungent, garden mustards grown for greens belong to this type. Black mustard (*B. nigra*) and white mustard (*B. alba*) are of interest mainly for their seeds.

Our word "mustard" is derived from the Old French *moustarde*, which in turn came from the Latin *mustum*, meaning must. In this sense "must" refers to the fresh juice or crushed pulp of grapes or other fruit, with which ground mustard seeds were mixed for use as a condiment.

Indian mustard has evolved into various types over so much of middle Asia that three centers of development have been found. It apparently originated in northwest India and adjacent areas, followed by further development in the secondary center of eastern India, Assam, and Burma, and also in China.

Our principal varieties are a large plain-leaved one, Elephant Ear, and two curly-leaved varieties, Fordhook Fancy and Southern Curled.

A number of "Japanese" mustards (*B. japonica*) are similar in growth habit and leaf and seed quality to some Indian mustards. But they differ basically in their hereditary make-up and do not cross readily with varieties of *B. juncea*.

Eggplant and Indian Mustard Trace Their Origin to Southern Asia. Leafy Indian mustard has adapted to cooler climes and thrives in any good garden soil; Eggplant (left) still prefers its weather warm. Besides purple and yellow forms, red, white, greenish, and striped eggplant are known. Its violet flowers are usually solitary.

161

Companion of Misery in Slave Ships

MOST OF OUR COMMON introduced plants came to the Americas by way of Europe, but the cowpea (*Vigna sinensis*) was brought from Africa to Jamaica about 1675 by slave traders. They carried stores of cowpeas to feed their tragic cargoes and also to plant for food in Jamaica.

Because of the plant's adaptability to tropical conditions and the high food value of its seeds, its culture spread over the West Indies in the early 18th century. It reached Florida from there about 1700, and was grown in North Carolina in 1714 and in Virginia in 1775.

Florida's edible varieties in 1775 were apparently much the same as our commonest kinds today. Some had well-rounded white seeds with a black "eye" (present variety Black-eye); others had seeds crowded so closely in the pod that the ends of the seeds were flattened (present varieties called "crowders," as Brown Crowder, Cream Crowder). These same kinds were described as common in the West Indies in 1756.

George Washington wrote in a letter in 1791 that "pease" (meaning cowpeas) were rarely grown in Virginia, but in 1797 he bought 40 bushels of seed for sowing on his plantation. Since the English pea is not suited to the hot South, the cowpea became more popular there and southerners applied the term "pea" to it instead of to *Pisum sativum* (page 156).

Cowpea is a name of American origin and was first used in print in 1798. When this crop was first grown in the United States, it was called "pease," "callicance," and later, "corn-field pease," because of the early custom of planting it between rows of field corn. It is often called "southern pea" and "southern field pea."

In India, the cowpea's land of origin, it has at least 50 common names, including *chowlee* (which sounds like cowpea but probably has no connection with our word), and *lubia*. The many old names, including one in Sanskrit, indicate that it was cultivated in prehistoric times. In India two related plants are catjang (*Vigna catjang*), a bush type, and asparagus bean (*Vigna sesquipedalis*), a climbing type.

In prehistoric times the cowpea was carried from India to Arabia and Asia Minor, thence down into Africa where an early form persists like a truly wild plant. The cowpea is grown to some extent in all parts of Africa where crops can be grown. It reached China before recorded history.

The early Greeks and Romans either were unfamiliar with this plant or failed to distinguish it among the various "peas" and "beans" about which they wrote. A Greek medical man of the first century of our era roughly described a plant that may have been the cowpea. Italians of the 14th century knew the plant, which could have reached them by way of Asia Minor or through Africa. Later its culture became common in the Mediterranean area, but not in northern Europe, where the climate is too cool.

Most of the edible varieties grown in the United States appear to have come from Africa along with the slaves, while most "field" varieties (used for stock feed and soil improvement) are more recent imports from India and China.

The Black-eye is by far our most important edible variety, although the crowders (Purple Hull, Lady, and others) are popular and are listed by seedsmen, especially in the South.

As a garden vegetable, the pods are usually harvested when the seeds are about fully grown and the pods beginning to fade in color, but before either begins to dry out. The "peas" are then shelled out of the pods and cooked with a piece of fat pork. They are of fine quality and highly nutritious, with a flavor all their own.

Is the cowpea a pea or is it a bean? It is distinctly different from both garden peas and garden beans. Botanically, it appears closer to plants we call beans than to those we call peas. In the South cowpeas are called simply "peas"; but dry seeds of the Black-eye variety are marketed for food as "beans"! The terms "pea" and "bean" thus are applied loosely, according to custom, rather than for any technical reason.

Cowpeas Are Just "Peas" in the South. Northerners Hardly Know Them. Before history was written the highly nutritious vegetable migrated from its native India to Africa and there became a common food. Slavers brought it to America. Black-eye is the most popular kind to eat; some varieties feed stock or enrich the soil.

Orientals Eat Giant Radishes

SCORES OF SPECIES of Chinese origin are grown as vegetables in China and Japan, but among them only radishes, Chinese cabbage, certain forms of mustard, and soybeans are commonly found in American gardens.

Radish (*Raphanus sativus*) gets its English, French, and Italian names from *radix*, the Latin word for root, especially a radish root. The technical name of the genus, *Raphanus*, is a Latinized form of the Greek *raphanos*, freely translated as "easily reared"—an apt name.

Many ancient as well as modern names indicate a long history of cultivation of this plant. China is believed to be the country of origin, since truly wild forms have been found there. Middle Asia appears to be a secondary center of development, to which the plant was introduced from China in prehistoric times.

Radishes were a common food in Egypt before the Pyramids were built. Ancient Greeks valued radishes so highly that they made small replicas of them in gold; beets were shown in silver and turnips in lead. Greeks of the third century B.C. wrote of radishes; one ancient Greek physician devoted a whole book to the plant.

Roman writers at the beginning of the Christian era described small, mild, early, round, and long forms (like ours), as well as the large later types weighing several pounds each.

The large, late radish (more like the Oriental than ours) seems to have been known in northern Europe and England much longer than the small, early kinds. It was described in Germany in the 13th century, but no small ones were recorded in that part of Europe until the mid-16th century. A German botanist in 1544 reported seeing radishes weighing 100 pounds.

Some have said the radish was unknown in England before 1548, but that seems unlikely in view of its early importance among Mediterranean peoples and ease of culture; it was common in England in 1586.

Radishes have been found as escapes from cultivation in Spain, Sardinia, and Greece.

They were seen in Mexico about 1500 and in Haiti in 1565, indicating that they were among the first European crops introduced into the Americas by the Spaniards. They were among the first grown by the English colonists and have been popular here ever since.

In China and Japan, most of the radishes are pickled in brine, much as we pickle cucumbers. Nearly a third of the tonnage of vegetables grown in Japan is radish (*daikon*). The radishes are pickled whole in large tubs, with rice hulls added to the brine, producing a rather attractive yellow color, but, to the Westerner, a most unattractive odor. Although low in food value, this pickled radish is a staple in the diet of every Japanese. Its salty, sprightly flavor adds zest to his drab diet of rice. Some Oriental varieties are grown for cooking. In China, one without an enlarged root is grown for the oil in its seeds.

In India the rat-tailed radish (*Raphanus caudatus*) is grown for its fleshy, edible seed pods, up to 12 inches long. In Egypt and the Near East one kind is grown for its tops, for greens. While the tops of our varieties are not unwholesome, they are far less palatable than leaves of turnips and other members of the cabbage clan.

Round radishes range in size from that of a cherry to that of a basketball; long ones range from finger size up to more than two feet long and five or six inches in diameter. These large kinds, grown in the Orient, are started in plant beds, then transplanted to field or garden, about a foot apart in the row. They are harvested in late autumn or early winter before danger of freezing. Oriental spring radishes are smaller. Oval or olive-shaped kinds are also known.

Radishes of white, red, or red and white are the commonest in America. Few gardeners grow the Round Black Spanish or Long Black Spanish, which are medium large, with black skin and a pungent, crisp, snow-white flesh. These, along with the faintly rose-colored China Rose and the White Strasburg, are so-called winter radishes, which can be stored the same as beets and turnips.

The Radish Is China's Most Popular Vegetable Gift to the Western World. Our little round or long, white or red kinds bear slight resemblance to the monstrous varieties the Chinese and Japanese grow for pickling and cooking. The radish is a member of the Crucifer family, as revealed by the shape of its four-petaled flowers.

Missionaries Sent Seeds of These to Europe

CHINESE CABBAGE (*Brassica pekinensis*) and Chinese mustard (*Brassica chinensis*) are so similar in their origin, history, and plant characters that it is best to deal with them together.

These common names are simply modern Anglo-American terms that indicate our impressions of what these two plants are. In America we often use the Chinese name *pe-tsai* for Chinese cabbage. Both vegetables, in effect, are mild-flavored "mustards." The first makes an erect, moderately compact, nearly cylindrical head suggesting a cabbage; the other's cluster of leaves does not form such a distinct head.

Chinese cabbage has been erroneously called celery cabbage because of the fancied similarity of shape of the head to a bunch of celery, but it is in no way related to celery.

Some varieties of Chinese mustard have neat leaf blades that are somewhat spoon-shaped, with long, white, erect leaf stalks, all forming a clump so dense that they were long confused with *pe-tsai* by Americans This type is only one of many leaf shapes and growth habits found within the species in the Orient.

Chinese cabbage and Chinese mustard are native to eastern Asia, possibly to Japan as well as to eastern China. They are mentioned in Chinese literature of the fifth century after Christ, but are much older than that. Since Indian mustard, also from China, has had world-wide popularity for centuries, it is strange that these two close relatives appear to have been spread so recently and to have remained of little importance in most lands. It may be because they are less adaptable to various soils and climates than Indian mustard (*Brassica juncea*).

These plants were unknown in Malaya and the East Indies until carried there by Chinese traders, who established "islands" of Chinese culture in foreign lands, very much as modern people do. Chinese writers of the 15th century said that Chinese cabbage and Chinese mustard, uncommon in Malaya, could be obtained in Malacca, where there was a Chinese colony.

The first record of these "mustards" in Europe was in 1751, but they remained oddities there for 100 years or more. During the 18th century European missionaries to the Orient sent seeds of these varieties to Europe, but they failed to become popular. The most prominent seedsman of France introduced Chinese cabbage to his country in 1845, but again it failed to catch on. The seed even became exhausted or lost and the plant was reintroduced later.

There has long been confusion over the botanical identity of Chinese cabbage, Chinese mustard, Indian mustard, and various closely related forms. For hundreds of years Chinese and Japanese have bred or selected an almost unbelievable diversity of varieties of each. It is impossible to determine to what species some of these things belong, merely upon seeing them in the garden; the numerous forms grade into one another with no clean line of demarcation. The distinction even between Chinese cabbage and Chinese mustard is often vague.

In America we prefer such varieties of Chinese cabbage as Chihli, which forms a long, slender, nearly cylindrical head that is relatively solid and weighs one to two pounds when trimmed. I was amazed at the enormously thick, squat types, weighing 10 to 12 pounds, that the Japanese prefer. The variety sold here as Pak Choy is not Chinese cabbage, strictly speaking, but Chinese mustard.

Chinese cabbage and Chinese mustard lack the distinctive pungency or "hotness" of Indian mustard when cooked as greens and therefore are most commonly eaten raw as salads. The mild, sprightly succulence of Chinese mustards in salads is delightful.

Chinese cabbage and Chinese mustard are annual plants that grow best in a mild climate. In hot weather they will shoot to seed without forming the attractive, productive plant desired. Over the warmer half of the United States they generally do better when planted in summer for an autumn crop than when planted in the spring.

Chinese Cabbage (Left) and Chinese Mustard Are Newcomers to the West. These delectable salad plants have taken root in Europe and America only within the past century, although cultivated in the Orient probably as long as the radish. Less pungent, less adaptable than Indian mustard, they are still little grown in this country.

Vegetable Soybeans Are New in America

THE SOYBEAN is not at present a widely popular garden vegetable in the United States. Its value is becoming appreciated, however, and it deserves to be used far more.

Soybeans (*Soja max*) have been grown in the Orient for more than 5,000 years, but they appear to have been known in the Western world a scant 250 years. It is puzzling, indeed, that this plant should have become established so late in western Asia, Europe, and the Americas, while many other species from China have been known and valued in the West for thousands of years. The soybean is still found wild in China.

The old Chinese name of this plant was *sou*, from which the names *soi*, *soy*, and *soja* doubtless were derived; hence our term "soybean." Supporting the belief in its great antiquity of culture, there are more than 50 distinct names for soybean in the Orient. Western names for the plant are remarkably similar as a result of its recent introduction.

The first written record about soybean is in a Chinese *Materia Medica* dating between 2900 and 2800 B.C. No mention is made in a European language before A.D. 1712, when a German traveler reported finding it in Japan in 1691 and 1692.

Missionaries returning from China in 1739 introduced the soybean into France, and it was grown in the Royal Botanic Gardens at Kew, England, as early as 1790. But it has remained an unimportant crop in Europe, grown there more as a vegetable than as a field crop, just opposite to common practice in the United States.

The soybean has been known in America more than 150 years. Benjamin Franklin sent seeds to this country from France in the late 18th century, and a sea captain who bought soybeans for his ship's stores introduced the plant about 1800. An encyclopedia published in Philadelphia in 1804 recorded that it was adapted to

China's Soybean Is One of the World's Great Food Plants. Vegetable varieties of soybean were little known in the United States a generation ago, though important in China and Japan for thousands of years. Field varieties are grown here by the millions of bushels for stock feed, meal, oil, plastics, and other industrial uses.

Pennsylvania and well worth cultivation there. In 1829 it was being grown at Cambridge, Massachusetts, where it was considered a luxury.

In 1853 a Government report referred to the soybean as the "Japan pea." It had been imported from Japan through San Francisco in 1850, then carried to Illinois and Ohio. When Commodore Perry returned from his famous expedition to Japan in 1854, he brought additional seeds. Between 1875 and 1900 a few more samples were imported, either from Europe or from Japan. But as recently as 1900 only eight varieties of soybean were known in the United States, and they were all field types rather than vegetable types.

More than 20 million acres of soybeans are grown annually in this country, chiefly for stock feed, oil for industrial purposes, flour for use in bakery and meat products, and proteins for making plastics. Foam fire-fighting materials are also prepared from soybeans. The field varieties are hardly suited for table use.

It was only about 30 years ago that many Americans began to learn about vegetable varieties of soybean; yet their use as a vegetable is at least 1,500 years old. They are gradually gaining favor in this country, and a few companies are canning the immature seeds. They can also be preserved by dehydrating or quick-freezing.

Seedsmen in this country now list several varieties suitable for fresh use as a vegetable. Among them are Bansei and Fuji for early harvest; Hokkaido and Jogun for midseason or late harvest; Seminole and Rokusun for culture in the South. The plants of most varieties are relatively large, so that the rows need to be two to two and one-half feet apart in the garden, with two to three inches between plants in the row. Since they are slow to reach harvest and are rather large-growing, they are not well adapted to very small gardens or to short, cool summers.

Soybean seeds are very rich in oil and in protein. Yields may not appear large, but the seeds, are a highly concentrated food with a distinct flavor and a smooth, buttery texture. Like most "new" foods, the soybean may require repeated trials to appreciate it. Gardeners should consult their local experts about varieties and ways to grow and use this ancient "new" vegetable.

How Fruit Came to America

BY JOHN R. MAGNESS

"JOHNNY," says the lady of the house, "here's a dollar. Run buy me a can of fruit salad and bring me the change."

Johnny knows where to go—the grocery store around the corner. It doesn't occur to him to ask where the grocer gets fruit salad. But if it should, the grocer too would know the answer: from the wholesaler, who, of course, buys it in turn from the packer. Obviously, it's a simple matter to trace a fruit salad back to its source.

Or is it?

Where did the packer get it? Here the story becomes complicated. Suppose the canned salad contains just a handful of the commonest fruits: part of a pear, a few grapes, half a dozen sweet cherries, some pieces of pineapple, and a few slices of peach. At home, Johnny's mother may garnish these with a little fresh apple, grapefruit, or orange.

To track just these few to the places where they are grown today would take much travel. The apple is likely to have come from Virginia, New York, Washington State, or perhaps from the Midwest, near the Great Lakes. The cherries are probably from Oregon or Washington; the grapefruit and orange from Florida or California; the peach, pear, and grapes from the Pacific coastal area; and the pineapple all the way from Hawaii.

But that is still only half the story. Peaches didn't always grow in California, nor apples in Washington. In fact, 500 years ago, before the first white settlers came, only the grape of all these common fruits had ever been seen or heard of in what is now the United States. The rest got here only after toilsome journeys lasting tens of centuries and starting in the farthest parts of the world.

Peaches and oranges came to us from China. It took them about 4,000 years, perhaps longer, to finish the trip. Apples, pears, and sweet cherries first appeared in the fertile, temperate, hilly land around the Black and Caspian Seas. Peoples of ancient civilizations there and in Europe knew and ate them centuries before Columbus or anyone else thought of sailing west to get to India.

Grapefruit? Five centuries ago there weren't any. There was, growing in the East Indies, a big, tough fruit, the shaddock. Eventually— sometime in the 1600's—it was to make a long voyage in a trading ship bound for the West Indies. There, by one of those strange tricks of Nature we call mutations, it would turn into a fruit like the one in our salad bowl.

Pineapples started in the Western Hemisphere; Columbus found them growing in the West Indies. But even this fruit had moved halfway across the Pacific to Hawaii before it was sent to our fruit salad packer.

The fruits we grow in America, in other words, didn't just spring up here naturally. They had to travel to get here, which, as a matter of fact, is natural, since Nature designed fruit especially to travel.

A man going for a walk plucks an apple from a tree, munches it as he walks, and then throws away the core. From the man's point of view, eating the meat on the apple is the important part of this operation. To the tree, however, the important thing is that he walked, and that he threw away the core.

In the struggle for survival, plants, like animals, have worked out tricks and devices to spread their seed. Or, to put it the other way around (but more accurately), those plants which evolved no such device were very likely to die out. Some developed seed pods which open explosively, scattering seeds for yards around. Others, like the dandelion, grew seeds on tiny parachutes which float in the wind. Still others evolved seeds which can survive long, wet trips in ocean currents.

Fruit plants, however, evolved a different method of distribution. Their seeds were covered with a layer of pulp or flesh which attracted animals and men because it was nourishing or had a pleasant flavor. Often, too, the skin covering the pulp was bright-colored and appealing. It is no accident that berries and cherries have been among the most widely distributed plants since prehistoric times. Their fruit was especially suited to birds, which could carry the seed farthest and fastest.

At first, men, like the other animals, simply picked and ate the wild fruit, propagating it accidentally. As time went on, however, they learned to dig holes and plant the seeds instead of discarding them, and to keep weeds and other plants cleared away from the spot where the new fruit was to grow. This was the beginning of horticulture.

Primitive man also quickly learned to pick out the seeds of the best plants—those which

171

bore most abundantly or produced food with the best flavor. This was scientific breeding in its earliest stages.

He found that with most of the plants we now classify as vegetables this system worked fairly well. These are the crops which we plant anew each year from seed, and which generally mature in a single season. They come fairly true from seed; that is, the offspring of any plant usually resemble the parent.

With fruits, however, this didn't work so well. One distinguishing feature of all crops we commonly call fruits is that they grow on plants that live and produce for a number of years. Many, in fact, must grow for several years before they bear fruit at all. This makes seed selection a slow and tedious process. Also, most of them do not come true to seed.

These early horticulturists soon found out that seed of a superior fruit tree—a peach, an apple, a pear, or almost any other—might or might not produce trees as good as its parent. More often it did not. And so men worked out a third important step in the science of fruit growing: what is now known as "vegetative propagation."

This was based on the discovery, made long before there were any historians to record it, that it was possible to plant a branch rather than a seed from a fruit tree. Sometimes the branch, or cutting, could be set directly in the soil, where it sprouted new roots. More often it was "planted," or grafted, into the stem of another and similar tree, letting the already growing roots supply it with food from the soil. In other cases, "suckers" instead of cuttings were planted, or even sections of roots.

The important fact was that whenever a tree or bush was propagated in this way, the new plant produced fruit with exactly the same characteristics as the parent; it was, literally, a "chip off the old block." Today virtually all the cultivated fruit we eat is taken from plants propagated in this way.

One of our most popular apples, the Winesap, has spread across the country by means of twigs or shoots budded or grafted into seedling apples. These shoots all trace originally to a single tree discovered more than two centuries ago. Because this one tree bore superior apples, it was transformed into thousands of trees which have produced millions of bushels of fruit.

If you eat grapes of a popular variety known as Thompson Seedless, you are eating fruit from a plant which first sprouted almost 1,000 years ago.

Naturally, selection and culture of fruit began in areas where men first moved haltingly toward civilization. Thus it is not surprising that, of the cultivated fruits we know today, the largest number can be traced to two broad regions where the earliest civilizations arose.

One region includes the sections of southeastern Europe and southwestern Asia stretching from the eastern Mediterranean to the Caspian Sea. From there, in addition to apples, came pears, cherries, figs, olives, and most of our plums and grapes.

The other is the part of central and southern Asia that stretches from China through Burma and eastern India southeast into the Malay Archipelago. There, thousands of years before the Christian era, men were eating and learning to cultivate peaches, apricots, bananas, mangoes, and, a little later, oranges and lemons.

As civilization spread from these areas to Europe and eventually around the world, men took their improved fruits with them, either as seeds or plants. When America was settled, the choicest kinds of fruits from Europe were transplanted to our shores. Even though the art of grafting was well known, and some grafted trees were brought over, most of the earliest plantings were seedlings. In many instances the Indians secured seed of the European fruits and planted them about their villages. Thus groves of fruit trees, mainly from seedlings, not only were established wherever there were white settlers, but moved westward even in advance of the settlements.

These seedling trees were highly variable. Occasionally one would be found bearing unusually good fruit. As the country became settled, these superior trees were propagated, given local names, and more or less widely tested. Many of our present varieties began this way. Others have been brought directly from older countries.

Not all the improvement and selection of varieties have been due to chance or to importations. A little more than a century ago, an intense interest in fruit breeding developed in this country. Private individuals began to cross varieties, grow the resulting seed to fruiting, and evaluate the fruit they got. Greatest interest was displayed in grapes, strawberries, raspberries, and American plums, but all fruits received some attention. Many excellent varieties resulted from such efforts.

A little later, after organization of the State agricultural experiment stations and the U. S. Department of

From This Graft an Apple Tree Will Produce a New Fruit. With a grafting tool (below) the pomologist inserts a twig from a newly developed variety of apple. Taking life and strength from the growing stock, the twig will become a limb and bear its own improved fruit. Such grafting is done early in spring when the stock's growth has started but the twig is still dormant.

The grafting operation is completed (above) by painting the sawed and slit end of the limb to seal out air. The waxy compound is not removed and sometimes clings to the limb for three or four years until growth pushes it off.

Willard R. Culver, National Geographic Photographer

Willard R. Culver, National Geographic Photographer

Agriculture (whose work, prior to the Presidency of Abraham Lincoln, was conducted by the Patent Office!), a number of such Government-supported stations began fruit-breeding work. This made possible more extensive and longer range work than could be conducted by private growers alone.

Today an even broader program of fruit improvement is under way in this country. Using new techniques discovered by geneticists, breeders sometimes even alter hereditary characteristics of the plant cells themselves and produce hybrids of plants which could never have been crossed naturally. In this way they work to combine superior flavor, large size,

174

and abundant production with such other qualities as resistance to disease, hardiness to cold, and late (or early) ripening. Production of just a few greatly improved varieties of berries, plums, apples, or grapefruit may pay the cost of research many times over.

Unfortunately, as fruits and fruit plants moved from continent to continent, they did not always travel alone. Insects or their eggs or larvae sometimes rode with them, hidden in the fruits themselves or in the leaves, bark, or roots. Other stowaways were the fungi, bacteria, and viruses which cause plant diseases.

Often, too, in the new land new pests were waiting, pests against which they had developed no resistance. As transportation improved and commerce increased, it became more and more difficult to keep these insects and blights localized.

A good example of the problem is provided by the phylloxera, or root louse, which feeds on the roots of native American grapes. In this country it causes little damage; the American plants are largely resistant to it. Taken to Europe, however, probably on the roots of American vines, it threatened to wipe out Europe's grape and wine industry. The European vines were saved only by grafting them on the roots of American grapes, a practice still followed today.

A more familiar example to most American gardeners is the Japanese beetle. About half a century ago it was transported from Asia to the eastern United States. Here, in the absence of natural enemies, it spread steadily. It still causes heavy damage to crops.

A virus disease of citrus, apparently carried in trees from Africa, has destroyed a large portion of the citrus orchards of South America. These have to be toilsomely replanted on rootstocks resistant to the disease. In recent decades strict regulations have been set up to control the spread of such diseases and pests to the United States.

Thus men, having undertaken the job of propagating and breeding fruit trees in order to harvest their food, have also been forced to take over a large part of the fight against their insect and disease enemies. The modern orchardist must know these pests, their life stories, how they pass the winter, when they invade the foliage and fruit.

He must know what materials to use and when to spray to control specific insects and blights. He uses mechanized equipment costing thousands of dollars to protect his trees. This includes power sprayers which can pump tens of gallons of liquid a minute over wide areas, and even planes and helicopters to fly low and dust treetops.

The cost of such equipment, combined with the superiority of the fruit it helps to produce, has tended more and more to concentrate fruit-growing into large commercial enterprises, gradually squeezing out the small, local farm orchard and the back-yard grower. Because of such heavy investments, commercial fruit growers can ill afford to lose a season's crop to frost, drought, heat, or humidity. Thus they confine their operations to areas best suited to the individual fruit.

This tendency to concentrate large orchards in fairly limited areas has led, in recent decades, to another revolution in the fruit industry—one mainly concerned with getting the fruit from grower to market. To move fresh fruit to consumers while it is still fresh, there are fast freight trains and huge fleets of refrigerated

railroad cars and trucks. Our can of fruit salad represents another solution. Largely in the last half-century, commercial fruit canning in the United States has grown to tremendous proportions. Americans eat millions of pounds of canned fruit each day.

Even more startling has been the growth of the frozen-fruit industry. Quick-freezing of fresh fruit for home use began commercially after World War I, but its great expansion has taken place only since the end of World War II. Frozen concentrated orange juice, for example, was developed in the late 1940's; now a major part of our orange production goes into it. Quick-frozen berries and peaches are available to consumers throughout the year.

A striking new development is the bulk shipment of refrigerated orange juice under vacuum by ocean-going tanker. Pumped ashore through stainless steel pipes, the juice is cartoned for delivery fresh with the morning milk.

So man spends millions of dollars and millions of hours of labor each year propagating and caring for his fruit trees and bushes, and picking, sorting, shipping, and preserving the fruit they bear. In return he gets a huge food crop which supplies him with a large part of the vitamins, minerals, and other nutrients he must eat to stay healthy.

This year, if you are a typical American, you will eat more than 150 pounds of fresh, canned, dried, and frozen fruit—making you the biggest consumer in the civilized world.

Americans are lucky to have within the borders of their country a wide variety of soils and climates suitable for growing fruit. The Pacific States particularly, with equable climates ranging from cool to subtropical, are ideal for orchards and vineyards and now produce about half the Nation's fruit.

Of the fruits pictured and described on the following pages, all but four (the banana, pineapple, papaya, and mango) are grown extensively in some part of the United States.

The Apple Is King

IN A GOOD YEAR about two-thirds of a bushel of apples is grown in the United States for every man, woman, and child. Every State, and virtually every temperate land in the world, grows some apples. Apples blossom throughout Europe and across Asia—in Russia, Siberia, China, Korea, and India; they also grow in Japan, Australia, New Zealand, and South America.

Flavor alone is not responsible for the fruit's popularity. Just as important is its hardiness. Some varieties can stand temperatures down to 40° below zero F. and will also grow in warm climates, provided there is a moderate winter to give the trees a rest.

America regards the apple and apple pie as its own, producing more of both than any other country. But the species from which our present varieties were developed, *Malus pumila*, probably started in southwestern Asia, between the Caspian and the Black Sea.

Long before recorded history, apples spread across Europe. Stone Age lake dwellers of central Europe not only stored fresh apples for eating but preserved them by cutting and sundrying them. The Greek writer Theophrastus mentions a number of varieties cultivated in Greece in the fourth century B.C. And according to mythology, an apple (albeit a gold one) was awarded to the goddess Aphrodite in what may have been the world's first beauty contest.

At the time America was discovered, apples were central and northern Europe's most important cultivated fruit. Inevitably the first settlers in temperate regions of the New World brought apples with them: the English to Virginia and New England, the Dutch to New York, and the French to Canada.

Once started, seedling apple plantings moved west faster than the white settlers. Some Indian tribes planted orchards around their villages. John Chapman, an itinerant missionary better known as Johnny Appleseed, roamed Ohio and Indiana early in the 19th century teaching the Gospel and planting apples. Apple seeds were planted at Vancouver, Washington, by 1817.

Though their ancestors came from Europe, most of our apple varieties started as seedling trees here in America. The apple does not come true from seed. A hundred trees grown from seed of a single tree will differ from each other and from the parent. Thus occasionally a chance seedling will prove better than previous varieties. If the new tree is named, and propagated by grafting or budding, it becomes a new variety.

In a fruit-growing community such a discovery is like striking oil or gold. Grateful citizens even erect monuments to the birth of a new apple. A pillar topped with a huge stone apple marks the spot where the first Baldwin apple tree was found in Wilmington, Massachusetts. Another in Dundas County, Ontario, Canada, stands where John McIntosh, while clearing forestland, discovered the apple that bears his name.

These and other varieties, such as the Winesap and Yellow Newtown, date back to colonial days. Others are more recent: the famous Delicious has been propagated only since 1895, and the Golden Delicious since 1916.

Major commercial apple areas in the United States are the irrigated valleys of the Pacific Northwest, particularly Washington; south and east of the Great Lakes, in New York, Ohio, and Michigan; and the foothills and valleys east of the Appalachian range, from North Carolina to New England.

Crab apple is a name popularly applied to trees that give small fruit (½ to 1½ inches in diameter), usually very acid and tart. These may be "native" (unimproved) species, or crosses of small-fruited species with cultivated varieties. Most crab apples grown for fruit in this country started as crosses of the Siberian species *M. baccata* with standard apples, and are generally called Siberian crabs. They are popular in Canada because they are hardy and ripen early.

In northern Europe crab apples often go into cider. American housewives like them for pickles and jelly. Many kinds of crab apple are also grown not for their fruit but as flowering shrubs.

Apples, Native to Southwest Asia, Came to America with Early Colonists. Small, sour crab apples (right) were hoarded in caves by Europe's Stone Age men. Centuries of cultivation produced today's big juicy varieties, as tasty raw as in steaming deep-dish pie.

Pears and Quinces: Butter and Jelly

"WHEN YOU DIVE into a pear," a fruit lover once remarked, "you never know whether you're going to strike water or sand."

The great variation in pears in our markets—from the softest and juiciest to the hardest and grittiest—can be blamed chiefly on a tiny bacterium with a musical name, *Erwinia amylovora*. But for *Erwinia*, the gritty sand pears probably would be little grown in the United States.

The common pear, *Pyrus communis*, like its cousin, the apple, seems to have come originally from western Asia. And like the apple, it was used as food by Stone Age men and improved by pre-Christian Greeks. Conquering Romans carried it with them in temperate parts of the Old World. Pear culture was common throughout Europe when America was discovered.

The pear trees brought to this country by early colonists at first produced abundantly. By 1771 the Prince Nursery on Long Island, greatest of colonial fruit nurseries, listed 42 varieties.

Meanwhile European horticulturists, particularly in France and Belgium, sought new and better varieties. In the 18th and 19th centuries many breeders named superior types, though two deserve particular credit. Nicolas Hardenpont (1705-44), a priest in Mons, Belgium, produced from quantities of seedling trees the first of the varieties with soft, melting flesh that gave the best pears the nickname "butter fruit." Later, Jean Baptiste van Mons (1765-1842), a physician in Leuven, Belgium, bred pears on a large scale and helped popularize some 40 superior types.

But as the improved varieties appeared in America, so did *Erwinia amylovora*. These bacteria invade the bark, roots, and other soft tissues of the tree, causing cankers and killing large limbs and eventually whole trees. The scorched appearance of the infected parts accounts for the popular name of the disease, fire blight.

It was observed in America as early as 1780. But not until a century later did Dr. Thomas Jonathan Burrill, a University of Illinois plant pathologist, single out the cause. As yet, no one has discovered an effective control, and pear blight still makes growing the quality "butter" pears of Europe hazardous east of the Rockies.

In eastern Asia another kind of pear had developed, *P. pyrifolia*, hard of flesh and with numerous "sand" or grit cells. These sand pears, still widely grown in China and Japan, reached the United States before 1840, by way of Europe. They proved quite resistant to fire blight, also to the teeth and palates of the consumers.

Hybrids of sand pears and European varieties soon appeared, starting as chance seedlings where trees stood adjacent in orchards. The most important, the Kieffer, first fruited in 1873. The hybrids now grown extensively in the eastern half of the United States are blight-resistant and better to eat than the original sand pears, but still inferior to the best European kinds. Research is under way to breed better blight-resistant varieties for eastern growers.

In the mild, dry-summered valleys of California, Oregon, and Washington, the best European varieties grow almost to perfection. Here grow most of the pears for canning and for sale as fresh fruit, about two-thirds of the national crop. Millions of bushels from these three States have been shipped back to the Low Countries of Europe, whence their ancestors came.

Pears are important in all temperate parts of Europe. France, Germany, Italy, and Switzerland lead in production. Part of the French crop is made into perry, a fermented pear cider. Argentina and Australia also have large crops.

The quince, *Cydonia oblonga*, is just a name on a jelly jar or a nugget in a fruitcake to most Americans. Closely related to the pear, it appears to be native to northern Persia, was known in Greece and Italy long before the Christian era, and was brought to this country by the earliest colonists. Though its low, gnarled trees once were widely grown in back-yard orchards, it has since fallen into disrepute. A few small commercial plantings satisfy the steady domestic demand for preserves and flavoring.

From Kashmir to Western Europe, Pears and Quinces Grew Wild Before History Began. Settlers brought them to the New World. Like most fruit trees, the best pears—Bartletts, Anjous, and others—are grown by grafts or cuttings from parent trees, not from seed. A blight limits most of our commercial crop to western States.

The Peach, Most Versatile of Fruit

WHAT FRUIT besides the peach can be eaten whole like an apple, sliced with cream, dried, stewed, pickled, spiced, canned, distilled into a fine liqueur, cooked into pie or jam—or frozen into delicious ice cream?

Due to its amazing versatility and unsurpassed flavor and texture, the peach ranks near the top in popularity in America. We show our high regard for the fruit by complimenting a young lady on her "peaches-and-cream" complexion; to describe the lady herself as a peach is also flattering, if less subtle.

Some ancient Chinese writers called the peach the tree of life, some the tree of death; others thought it symbolized longevity. The pink peach blossom was associated with feminine promiscuity, and growers were warned not to plant peach trees near windows of a lady's boudoir.

"Peach" is based on a Latin word meaning Persian. The scientific name, *Prunus persica*, also implies Persian origin; in fact, peaches used to be called "Persian apples." But the 2,000-year-old belief that Persia was the home of the peach has not withstood scientific scrutiny.

Lack of mention in early Hebrew or in Sanskrit literature suggested the fruit was unknown from Persia to western India about 1500 B.C. And in China, botanists found many types which appeared native there, yet had all the characteristics of the western fruit. Also, Chinese literature makes note of peaches before 2000 B.C. Most experts therefore now agree that China is undoubtedly the native home of the peach. The species probably ranged from Turkistan as far as the eastern coast.

Exactly how and when it reached Persia is not known, but it probably traveled from China along caravan routes of the pre-Christian era. By 332 B.C. it reached Greece, where it was described as a Persian fruit. Virgil (70–19 B.C.) was the first Roman to mention the peach. Its culture subsequently spread over temperate parts of Europe. The Spaniards probably planted the first peaches in the New World; by 1571 three types were growing in Mexico. The French in Louisiana, the English at Jamestown and Massachusetts, and others planted peaches soon after settlement. Indians carried the new food supply inland.

Practically all varieties now grown in this country started here, most through chance discovery of superior trees among seedlings. In the past 50 years State and Federal experiment stations and some private researchers have been systematically breeding peaches to develop quality varieties.

Some of the best thin-skinned, soft-fleshed ones, like the Cumberland and Golden Jubilee, are so delicate they may be damaged in handling and shipping long distances to market. The peach is thus a favorite in small orchards and even back yards.

Besides trouble with diseases and insects, the peach is not the hardiest of trees. Buds are often killed by temperatures of 10° below zero F., and drops to 20° below frequently kill the trees. Most varieties also need a fairly long dormant season to start normal growth in spring.

Peaches do best here on the Pacific coast, especially in California; along the Atlantic seaboard from Georgia to Massachusetts; and in the Great Lakes region of New York, Ohio, and Michigan. They also thrive in Europe, Asia, South Africa, Australia, and South America.

The nectarine is a fuzzless peach not widely grown in the United States. Indistinguishable from the peach in tree, leaf, or flower, it has fruits similar in shape and pit, or stone. Both have white-, yellow-, and red-fleshed varieties.

Nectarines are usually smaller, firmer-fleshed, more aromatic, and richer-flavored than the peach. They originate as true breeding mutations of the peach, and have been esteemed in the Old World for more than 2,000 years. But because their smooth skin makes them vulnerable to insects, disease, and cracking, they are not as successful as peaches in the humid eastern United States. They reach market in limited quantities, mainly shipped from the western States.

Peaches Were Cultivated in China More than 4,000 Years Ago. Spanish settlers planted the first peaches in America before 1600. They now rank third among our tree-grown fruit. Nectarines (right) are smooth-skinned peaches, easier to eat but harder to grow.

Two Stone Fruits from the Orient

APRICOTS AND JAPANESE PLUMS belong to the great group of stone fruits, or drupes, which includes fruit ranging in size from cherry to peach, all containing a single hard, woody pit. These two are considered together because both are believed to be Chinese in origin. Their routes around the world, however, were quite different, as are the ways in which we eat them.

The apricot, though juicy and aromatic when fresh, is one of the fruits which most Americans know mainly as dried or canned.

The apricot reached the Mediterranean countries before the time of Christ. Alexander the Great supposedly carried it to Greece after his conquest of southwestern Asia in the fourth century B.C. It was long said to have come from Armenia, hence its botanical name, *Prunus armeniaca*. More recent botanical and language research, however, reveals no name for the fruit in either the Hebrew or Sanskrit languages, as would be expected had the fruit been present in southwest Asia as these languages developed.

On the other hand, the Chinese used a character believed to represent the apricot in writings earlier than 2000 B.C. And in China today apricots are found which have all indications of being truly indigenous.

Thus it is now generally believed that the apricot originated in central and western China, and that it had been carried to southwest Asia before Alexander's time. Pliny stated it reached Italy about 100 B.C. It had spread throughout Europe's temperate parts, including England, before the discovery of America.

The earliest Spanish settlers apparently brought the apricot to the New World. It throve in the drier parts of Mexico. Seedlings were planted at the California missions in the 18th century, and named varieties from Europe were introduced before 1850.

The English also grew them in Virginia; Capt. John Smith reported them thriving there in 1629. However, the apricot has never proved well adapted to the climate of the eastern States.

The name "apricot" comes from a Latin word *praecoquum*, meaning early ripe. Because it blooms very early, its blossoms are almost always killed in the East by spring frosts. The fruit also tends to crack badly and decay in warm, rainy weather. Apricot growing in the United States is therefore largely confined to the area west of the Rockies, with California producing by far the largest part of the crop. Washington, Oregon, and Utah also produce commercial quantities of apricots.

Little can be said of the background of the highly colored, juicy, spicy fruit of the species *P. salicina*, known in this country as Japanese plums. Certainly they did not originate in Japan. Japanese horticulturists say they were introduced into Japan from China some 200 to 400 years ago. It seems almost certain their native home is in China, perhaps in the southwest part, a region little explored by western botanists.

These plums first reached America about 1870, the year a fruit grower of Vacaville, California, imported trees from Japan. They quickly attracted attention and propagation started.

Luther Burbank, the great plant breeder, gave American names to varieties he imported and to selections from the many seedlings he grew. More than any other man, Burbank was responsible for the great interest in Japanese plums and their rapid spread.

These plums apparently were unknown in Europe prior to their introduction into this country. In recent years they have been tested in temperate countries throughout the world.

They are grown here to a limited extent in many States. Though subject to killing by early spring frost, they withstand summer heat and rain better than European plums, and surpass in quality most of our native kinds. They cross with most native American plums, and promising hybrids are being developed. The large, colorful plums on fruit stands from mid-June through August are mainly Japanese or, more accurately, Oriental plums, from California.

Apricots and Japanese Plums Traveled East and West from China. Capt. John Smith reported newly planted apricots thriving in Virginia in 1629. Today most of our crop comes from California. The "Japanese" plum is also Chinese, but first reached our west coast from Japan. No plum appears to be native to Japan.

Plums and Prunes from Europe and Western Asia

THE MOST IMPORTANT commercial plums grown in the United States came from southwestern Asia by way of Europe. They belong to the species *Prunus domestica* and are of three main types.

First in quantity and market value are the drying plums, or prunes. These are fairly large, firm-fleshed, meaty plums with a high sugar content. They are dried in the sun or in dehydrators in tremendous quantities and form our familiar dried breakfast prunes. California leads in production. Some varieties of this type are also grown for fresh fruit or for canning, chiefly in Oregon, Washington, Idaho, and Michigan.

The second type is popularly called the Greengage or Reine Claude group. These fruits are light green to golden yellow when ripe, nearly round, and the flesh adheres to the pit. They are generally softer fleshed than the prune group and are not suitable for drying. Many excellent varieties are widely grown in home gardens and in small commercial orchards, but they are not marketed extensively.

The third type, varying from the second mainly in size and shape, is the Egg plum. The fruit is very large, generally long-oval in shape, sometimes with a neck at the stem end. Its color varies from yellow to purple.

One other species which came by way of Europe is *P. insititia*, the small, nearly round to oval Damson type (named for the city of Damascus), greatly prized for jam and plum butter.

The *domestica* plums are commonly called European, but botanists report the species as native to western Asia, apparently from south of the Caucasus Mountains to the Caspian Sea.

Plums do not thrive in tropical or subtropical climates. The Egyptians left no record of them. The first Roman writer to mention them was Pliny, who described several kinds briefly and referred to "a vast number of varieties."

Asiatic Plums Grow in a Bewildering Variety of Shapes, Colors, and Sizes. Americans grow Greengage and large yellow Egg plums to eat fresh; both kinds are native to western Asia. Smaller Asiatic reds and purples, when dried, become prunes. Tart blue Damsons, from western Asia and Europe, make good jam.

Europe's major plum-growing areas developed north of the Mediterranean countries, and apparently the growing of *domestica* type plums there is rather recent. Historians say prunes were introduced into Hungary from Turkistan late in the 15th century. All Balkan countries are now important prune producers.

The Reine Claude group is named for Queen Claudia of France, whose husband, Francis I, ruled at the time of their introduction into that country, about 1500. A little later they were introduced into England by Sir William Gage, whence came the name Greengage. Thus it may be presumed that these plums were not widely grown in Europe before America was settled.

Little is known about their introduction into America. The French brought them to the Maritime Provinces of Canada, and undoubtedly the English brought them to their colonies. *Domestica* plums, however, were not important in American horticulture until after the Revolution, and did not become a major crop until the Pacific States were settled.

These plums and prunes bloom early in the spring, and in many locations are subject to killing frost. The fruit cracks badly and decays under heavy rainfall conditions. In the eastern States only the most favored fruit sections, such as the lake areas of New York and Michigan, have much success with them. The Pacific coast climate, on the other hand, is ideal for maximum production, and in some areas for sun-drying.

Damson plums apparently were native not only to western Asia but to most of Europe. Their pits have been found on the sites of the lake dwellings of Switzerland. The recorded history of the Damson is older than that of other species. Greek poets of the sixth century B.C. mention them. The selected, improved varieties, however, appear to have stemmed from western Asia.

The Damson types were introduced into the Colonies and, prior to the Revolution, apparently were grown more widely and successfully than the *domesticas*. These tart, spicy plums, now widespread in parts of the country having a moderate climate, are produced mainly in home gardens and for local markets. Damson jam or plum butter is esteemed by most who know it.

185

American Plums, Fruit of the Pioneers

NATIVE AMERICAN PLUMS belong in this story of fruits, not because they are important in commerce, but because of the place they filled in the diets of early settlers. From New England to Florida, the colonists found wild plums. As wagon trains rolled westward, pioneers discovered them growing in all sections to the Rockies and scattered beyond to the Pacific.

No other native tree fruit is so widely distributed here as the plum, some form being found in every State in the Union. While our native wild plums are not generally of high dessert quality, most make very good jam, jelly, and plum butter. They offered a welcome variety to the often monotonous diet of the pioneers.

New England colonists found two principal kinds. The hardy Canadian plum, *Prunus nigra*, still grows throughout New England and New York, around the Great Lakes, over much of Minnesota, and into Canada. Its large, pink-tinged flowers are unusual: plum flowers are generally smaller, and pure white or green tinged. The fruit is oval to oblong, a little over an inch long, and varies from crimson to orange-yellow. It ripens in late August and September.

Indians picked and dried these fruits; quantities are still gathered from the wild. Cultivated varieties derived from them are among the most dependable fruits for our northern areas.

The second plum found by the colonists was *P. maritima*, a small bush bearing nearly round fruit about two-thirds of an inch in diameter. This beach plum grows in a narrow belt from southern Maine to Virginia and is prized for jam. Of native plums it resembles the European Damson most, and many enjoy its spicy flavor.

A third great species, *P. americana*, spreads over about half the United States, from New York to Montana and south to Louisiana and Mississippi. Known in most sections simply as wild plum, it is also called Red plum, Yellow plum, Horse plum, Hog plum, Goose plum, August plum, and in the far South, Sloe. The fruit ripens mainly in July in the South, and in September in the North. The plums are generally nearly round, reddish-orange to red, and one inch or less in diameter. From this species have come many varieties of value, especially in the western Plains States.

The Chickasaw plum, *P. angustifolia*, is native in the southern States from Maryland to the Gulf and west to Kansas and Texas. The fruit is oval to spherical, usually bright red, but sometimes yellow. It does not survive in the North. The closely related Sand plum of the western Plains is a most valued fruit in Kansas and Nebraska.

Two lower Mississippi Valley species are valuable as native fruits and as sources of cultivated varieties. Both are found from Tennessee and Kentucky west to Kansas and Oklahoma. *P. hortulana* is late ripening, its fruit nearly round, about one inch in diameter, and red to yellow. The Wild-goose plum, *P. munsoniana*, ripens early, fruit is round to oval, and bright red. Both bloom late, so the blossoms are likely to escape spring frosts.

One other species deserves mention because its quality closely approaches European plums. *P. subcordata*, the Pacific or Western plum, grows in the foothills from central California to central Oregon. The fruit ripens late, is globular, red to purple, about one inch in diameter, and is used extensively for jam and jelly.

Colonists along the eastern seaboard gathered wild plums but made little effort to improve them, perhaps because good European varieties could be grown in the central and northern colonies at least. Not until settlers crossed the Mississippi were native plums of special merit selected, named, and planted in home orchards.

During the last half of the 19th century, hundreds of such selections were made and named. Many represented little improvement and soon passed out of use. Private breeders and State experiment stations continued to improve these plums, making available varieties of great value for home and local market growing in the Plains States, the North Central States, and in the South, areas where European plums do not thrive.

Small-fruited American Plums Are Cultivated Chiefly in the Plains States. Pioneers found them growing wild on beaches, hills, and fields across country. Larger imported plums have crowded these "natives" out of most markets, but they are still gathered wild in many areas.

"Loveliest of Trees, the Cherry..."

ROUND, PLUMP, AND ABUNDANT, cherries have for centuries been a symbol of ripeness and sweetness. Americans confirm this high esteem for the richly flavored fruit by the huge amounts they consume fresh or in pies, candies, preserves, beverages, and assorted drugstore delicacies. As for abundance, a single tree has been known to yield 2,000 pounds of fruit in one year.

Cherry species are plentiful throughout the northern Temperate Zone, from Japan throughout Asia and Europe to our own Pacific coast. Asiatic species contributed the famous flowering cherries of Japan, now flourishing in our own Capital and many American gardens and parks.

The fruit of a few American species are gathered to a limited extent, particularly chokecherries and sand cherries in the Plains and Rocky Mountain States. But the two species that furnish our commercial cherries appear to have originated in the Eurasian area centering about the Dardanelles and extending westward from the Caspian Sea through the Balkan countries.

The cherry, *Prunus avium*, spread throughout temperate Europe as far as Britain before the beginning of civilization there. A favorite of birds, this species is commonly known as bird cherry. Pits found in the caves of central Europe indicate that man gathered sweet cherries as early as the Stone Age. The sour or pie cherry, *P. cerasus*, seems to have spread more slowly, and perhaps mainly through human migrations.

Apparently the earliest reference to cherries is by Theophrastus, the Greek "Father of Botany," who described the trees and fruit about 300 B.C. Pliny, in first century Italy, described 10 kinds. These appear to have been types, rather than varieties as we regard them today. He also mentioned the cherry's having been taken to Britain. Marcus Terentius Varro discussed grafting of cherries and implied that neither cherry culture nor grafting was new when he wrote his book on farming about 50 B.C.

Thus cherry culture was apparently under way in a number of European countries by the beginning of the Christian era. But not until the 16th century did variety names appear.

If cherries were planted by the Spaniards in the West Indies and Florida, they did not thrive. But soon after the arrival in America of English, French, and Dutch settlers European varieties were growing in the cooler climates from Newfoundland to Virginia. In 1629, only nine years after the Pilgrims landed, the Red Kentish cherry was cultivated in Massachusetts. According to tradition, one Virginia farmer, Augustine Washington, valued his cherry trees only slightly less than the veracity of his son George.

Cherries advanced westward with the settlers. Spanish missionaries took them to California when that State was part of Mexico. Cherries were a part of the covered wagon load of named fruit varieties that pioneer horticulturist Henderson Luelling took to Oregon in 1847. This was the start of the West's great sweet cherry industry.

The cherry thrives best in moderate, rather cool climates. The sour cherry tolerates summer rainfall and winter cold better than the sweet, which cracks and rots when rains occur near ripening time. Sweet cherry production therefore centers in the States west of the Rockies, where summers are dry and winters generally moderate.

Sour cherries grow throughout the northern half of the country, except in the coldest areas of the Plains States. Greatest production is around the Great Lakes, with Michigan, New York, and Wisconsin leading. Neither sweet nor sour varieties are adapted to the hot, often humid South.

Our important sour cherry varieties are direct importations from Europe; no important varieties have been developed here. Several sweet varieties, on the other hand, originated here as chance seedlings, including the large, nearly black Bing and Lambert, the leading fresh market kinds.

Sour cherries are mainly marketed canned or frozen, for use in pies and preserves. Sweet cherries are popular fresh in midsummer. They are also canned commercially, and are the principal source of maraschino cherries.

Birds Spread Cherry Seeds Across Asia, Through the Balkans and Western Europe. We cultivate sweet cherries, like the Bing and Napoleon, as dessert fruit; sour ones like the Montmorency for pies and canning. Some Asiatic varieties, such as the Japanese flowering cherries, are prized chiefly for their showy blossoms.

Fruit of the Vine

ONE WAY TO GET an idea of the scope of world grape production is to start with California. On a little over half a million acres, Californians grow up to 3,000,000 tons of grapes a year—more than nine-tenths of all wine, raisin, and table grapes sold in this country. A single vineyard in Cucamonga Valley covers 5,000 acres.

Yet California produces less than ten percent of the world's grape supply and only about three to four percent of its wine. Grape growing is the world's biggest fruit industry.

Used mostly for wine, grapes are produced in tremendous quantities in the Mediterranean countries and in all other countries having moderately dry summers and equable temperatures. Both grape culture and the art of wine making were known to men before recorded history.

The Old World grape, *Vitis vinifera*, has been cultivated so long that its place of origin cannot be accurately determined. Best evidence, however, indicates it originally centered in the area about the Caspian and Black Seas, the great cradle of deciduous fruits. From there the seed was spread naturally by birds and mammals, and by the hand of prehistoric man.

Grape seeds found on Swiss lake-dwelling sites date to the Bronze Age. Others were discovered in Egypt's oldest tombs; the Egyptians evidently grew grapes and made wine 6,000 years ago. The oldest Hebrew, Greek, and Roman writings all refer to grapes and wine making.

The first European visitors to North America, the Norse voyagers, found native grapes so abundant that they called the country Vinland. Settlers in Virginia found great vines climbing over the trees, especially along the streams. But because of the poor quality of the wild grapes, every effort was made to transplant superior European vines. Almost every colony had laws to encourage grape growing. Hundreds of vine-yards were set, and skilled French vine growers were brought over. Settlers were even penalized for failing to plant grapes, and rewarded for success in vine growing and wine making. Yet no one did well with Old World grapes. In the "vineyard paradise" of the Colonies fungus and insects attacked and destroyed them. Even with today's insecticides and fungicides, the Old World grape does not thrive in the humid East.

In the West, the picture was far different. The Spaniards established a colony in New Mexico in 1598 and missions in California beginning in 1769. There the Old World grape flourished in the dry growing season and mild winters. Its production today is limited largely to the southwestern States; most varieties are direct imports. About half of these grapes are dried for raisins. Large quantities are made into wine and thousands of carloads are shipped fresh.

All other sections of this country grow varieties derived in part or entirely from native species. Muscadine varieties derived from the species *V. rotundifolia* are best adapted to the South. Highly disease-resistant, they have a tough skin, and are borne in very small clusters. Areas farther north grow varieties derived from *V. labrusca*, such as Concord and Niagara.

The American grapes withstand winter better than do Old World grapes. Considered generally less suitable for wine, they are the only kinds used for grape juice, and are superior to the *vinifera* grape for jellies and jams. They have a less meaty pulp than most Old World varieties, so are less suitable for raisins.

The root louse phylloxera, native to eastern America, was accidentally taken to Europe at least a century ago. For a time it threatened the existence of grape growing in many European regions. American species are resistant to this sucking insect, so most European vineyards are now grown on roots partly or wholly of American stock—stocks also used for Old World varieties in California and in many other regions of the world. Thus today the grapes of East and West are truly joined in the world's grape production. American varieties have also spread to other world areas where, because of winter cold or humidity, the *vinifera* grape is poorly adapted.

The World Grows More Grapes Than Any Other Fruit; Most Go Into Wine. Grapes are native to most temperate lands, but Asiatic types (left) make up 98 percent of commercial production. Of native American grapes (right), purple Concord is grown most. Our disease-resistant stocks gave new life to Old World vineyards.

191

Dates Provide Food in Desert Lands

SAID MOHAMMED: "There is among the trees one that is pre-eminently blessed, as is the Moslem among men; it is the palm."

Small wonder that desert dwellers from Arabia and Egypt to Algeria and Morocco call the date palm blessed. The fruit, containing more than half its weight in sugar and smaller quantities of fat and protein, is one of the most important food sources in a generally barren land. The tree furnishes shade; the leaves make baskets, matting, and bags; the fiber, rope. The roasted stones, or pits, substitute for coffee.

Old and nonproductive palms are tapped to draw off the sap, from which a toddy is made, called in ancient cuneiform inscription "the drink of life." Finally, the trunks are used as fuel.

Origin of the date palm, *Phoenix dactylifera*, is unknown. Certainly it is one of the oldest food plants. Plant remains, traditions, and the oldest writings indicate it grew in Arabia, Babylonia, and Egypt long before history began.

The date palm will grow wherever temperatures do not go lower than 5° to 10° F., but successful fruit production is largely limited to areas having very dry summer and fall seasons. As the fruit approaches maturity, even a small amount of rain and humid weather will cause it to mold and sour. Although grown in desert countries, date palms require the abundant soil moisture provided by springs, oases, or irrigation.

Present Old World centers of date growing are the same as in earliest times: Iran, Iraq, Arabia, Egypt, Libya, and Algeria. Spain grows some dates, but in general date culture is meager north of the Mediterranean, where rainfall and humidity are limiting factors.

No one knows exactly when date palms were first planted in the United States. Spanish missionaries planted seeds around the missions in the Southwest before 1800. But the real beginning of date culture was 1890, the year the U. S. Department of Agriculture had some of Egypt's better varieties planted in tubs and shipped to this country. Later, plantsmen from the Department visited all important date-growing countries, secured offshoots of the better varieties, and established them. Commercial firms followed with larger importations of the better kinds.

Superior date varieties can only be propagated by the offshoots, or "suckers," which develop from the base of relatively young palms. The suckers, much like those that form near the base of corn plants, may be cut off when three to five years old. Since each palm produces only a few, the multiplication of superior dates is a slow process.

Our date industry centers in the interior desert valleys of southern California and Arizona, which have intensely hot, dry summers and autumns much like Arabia and North Africa. The greatest concentration of planting is in California's Coachella Valley, northwest of the Salton Sea. Even with some 5,000 acres of date palms in production, this country still imports quantities of the fruit from southwest Asia, chiefly Iran.

Date varieties are of three kinds: soft, semidry, and dry. Soft dates, used extensively in date confections, are richly flavored, but difficult to ship and handle. Semidry dates are the ones usually seen here in the markets. The dry dates, little grown or sold in this country, are relatively hard-meated, sweet, and nonperishable; they are a basic food in Arab countries.

Because of our intensive scientific cultivation of the date, Old World countries now look to us for technical information on date culture. The U. S. Department of Agriculture has maintained a research station at Indio, California, almost from the start of date culture here.

Date growing involves tedious hand work as well as mechanization. Individual bunches, which may contain 1,000 or more dates, are sometimes wrapped in heavy paper to guard against insects, birds, or dampness. Pollination may be done by tying male flower strands into female flower clusters with rubber bands, or with a pollen duster. Helicopters have been hired to fly low over date treetops and fan away moisture.

Tall Date Palms Shade Green Oases in Deserts of Egypt and Arabia. Growing wherever there is moisture for their roots, dates have provided desert dwellers with food, shade, and fuel since Biblical times. The sizable date industry in California and Arizona began in 1890 with imported trees.

Olives, Oil-bearing Fruit from the Mediterranean

IN CROWDED COUNTRIES, or those where conditions are not suitable for extensive meat production, men turn to plants for the oil they must eat to live. In lands bordering the Mediterranean Sea, the olive tree supplies much of this need. From 20 to 60 percent of a ripe olive is oil. Men extract almost a million tons of oil a year from olives.

In Spain, which leads the world in olive oil production, six percent of agricultural production is in olives. In Greece the proportion runs as high as 18 percent. Italy ranks olives second only to grapes in importance; olives are the leading tree crop in Portugal, and the Portuguese consume nine-tenths of the oil they produce.

The olive is another fruit that may be traced beyond recorded history. Earliest Hebrew books mention the olive under the name *sait* or *zeit*, and the dove returning to Noah's Ark with an olive leaf is a story familiar to all. The olive was cultivated for its oil from the beginning of agriculture not only in Palestine but in Syria, Egypt, Greece, and, a little later, in Rome.

The ancients used the oil for food, medicine, and for anointing their bodies. In Rome a favorite saying was that a long and pleasant life depended on two fluids, "wine within and oil without." Olive oil was also burned in lamps.

Today the wild olive, *Olea europaea*, is found from western India through southwest Asia and all around the Mediterranean. We cannot be sure that it is truly native throughout that range, for in certain fringe areas the trees may be escapes from cultivation. Language research indicates that the true center of the olive species was probably the region from Syria to Greece.

The olive requires a long, warm growing season for its fruit to mature, and temperatures down to 10° or 15° F. injure the tree. Thus in Europe its growth is limited to countries around the Mediterranean.

The Spaniards apparently introduced the olive into America. While it did not thrive in the humid climate and acid soil of the West Indies and Florida, it grew well in the drier air of Mexico. It was introduced into California with the first missions. Since then, other valuable varieties have been brought in from Europe.

Large areas in the southwestern United States can grow olives successfully, but the great amount of hand labor needed, particularly in harvesting the fruit, has prevented large-scale cultivation here. This country therefore continues to import olive oil and green olive pickles from southern Europe, mainly Italy and Spain.

Only California and, to a limited extent, Arizona have an olive industry. This is based primarily on olives for pickling. Oil is extracted from fruit which fails to grow large enough for that purpose.

The olive, green when immature, turns black as it ripens. For green olive pickles, therefore, the fruit is picked early; for black olive pickles, it is allowed to mature on the tree but not become soft ripe. For oil, the fruit is allowed to ripen fully.

Olives fresh from the tree, green or ripe, are intensely bitter. In the pickling process the fruit is soaked first in lye solution to destroy the bitter taste. Thoroughly washed to remove the lye, ripe olives are next soaked in strong salt solution. (They can be held for a long period in brine, but then should be soaked in fresh water overnight to remove the excess salt.) After salting, they are canned under steam pressure at a temperature of at least 240° F. for 60 minutes.

In preparing green olive pickles, variations in the process develop special flavors.

Methods of extracting oil vary greatly from one country to another and depend in part on what the oil is to be used for. In some cases fruit is first crushed by rollers, then squeezed in presses, which may be simply flat boards with stones on top, or costly hydraulic machinery. Since the oil is in the pulp, stones are sometimes removed before pressing. If the oil is to be eaten, speed is essential between harvesting and pressing; oil left in bruised olives soon grows rancid.

In Mediterranean Countries the Olive Provides the Fat of the Land. Symbol of peace and wealth to the ancients, the fruit probably was first cultivated in Greece. Romans sometimes collected olive oil, instead of money, as taxes. Spanish missionaries planted our first olives in California, where domestic production now centers.

To Ancient Man, Figs Were a Sacred Fruit

IN AMERICA figs are eaten as a luxury, a sweet dessert, or a morsel in a fancily wrapped box of gift fruit. In some Mediterranean lands, however, figs are basic to the diet.

Legends reveal their importance in ancient times. The Romans considered the fig, *Ficus carica*, a gift of the god Bacchus. In southwestern Asia, Egypt, Greece, and Rome, figs were regarded as sacred. Their significance in Hebrew life shows repeatedly in the Bible, beginning with the story of the Garden of Eden. A fig-harvesting scene appears on the wall of a 12th dynasty Egyptian grave (*c.* 1989–1776 B.C.).

The species from which the cultivated fig came apparently had ranged from Syria westward to the Canary Islands. Fossil remains in France and Italy indicate that figlike plants grew there long before the Stone Age.

Figs probably were first cultivated in ancient Arabia and Egypt; doubtless the sweeter, better kinds were selected and propagated with the beginning of agriculture there. They were prized in Crete in 1500 B.C., and in Greece a little later. The Greeks even had an inkling of fig pollination. Aristotle, in the fourth century B.C., recorded that the young fruit would drop unless visited by insects, but he did not fully understand why.

Figs were introduced into America by the Spaniards. Varieties sent from Spain to Hispaniola in 1520 were bearing well in 1526. By the late 16th century, figs were abundant in Peru, and were established at St. Augustine, Florida. Capt. John Smith reported in 1629 that "Mistress Pearce" of Jamestown, Virginia, harvested "neere a hundred bushels of excellent figges."

In California the fig, like many other fruits, dates from the establishment of the mission at San Diego in 1769. The variety planted there, now called Mission, is still the leading black fig grown in the State. Although figs were widely planted in California gardens before 1885, commercial cultivation started only about then. Today California leads in United States production. Figs also are grown commercially in Texas, and as a garden fruit elsewhere in the South.

The fig is a semihardy tree which sheds its leaves in winter. When fully dormant, the trees will stand temperatures down to 10° F. without serious injury. Temperatures below 5° kill them to the ground, but in most cases new shoots will sprout from the roots.

Many varieties of figs will set fruit without pollination. The choicest of the white, drying varieties, however, belong to the Smyrna type, and these must be pollinated by a process called caprification.

Trees of this type were planted in California late in the last century and grew well, but the fruit dropped before maturing. Caprifigs, the trees used for pollinating this type in Europe and Asia, were brought into the State. But the small wasp, the *Blastophaga*, that carried the pollen into the fruit, was missing and early efforts to introduce it failed. Finally in 1899 the U. S. Department of Agriculture imported caprifig fruits containing Blastophaga wasps. Since then, production of Smyrna varieties in California has been successful.

These wasps breed in caprifigs. At the proper time, the caprifigs are gathered with the wasps in them and hung in small bags in the fruit-bearing trees. The female wasps crawl out, becoming covered with pollen as they do so. They crawl into the fruit of the Smyrna varieties and, in their search for a place to lay eggs, pollinate the flowers.

Italy is the world's leading producer of figs, most orchards being located south of Naples, and on Sicily. Turkey ranks second. Spain, the United States, Algeria, Greece, and Portugal all have major industries. Many other countries produce figs on a smaller scale.

Most of the world's figs are marketed in dried form; some are canned or preserved. Fresh figs are esteemed in countries where they are grown, but they are difficult to ship to distant markets.

Cultivated Since Antiquity, Figs First Grew in Mediterranean Lands. Ancients revered them; Americans consider them a delicacy; but in parts of Europe figs are known as the poor man's food. Spanish missionaries planted them in California in 1769, but the choicest varieties would not fruit until a special wasp was imported from Algeria to pollinate them.

Gold Flows from Orange Groves

THE ORANGE INDUSTRY in the past half century has undergone one of the most astounding booms in the history of agriculture. In 1900 oranges were a luxury, a Christmas treat, or a special dessert in most of the United States.

Today oranges are for sale everywhere the year round. Orange juice, fresh or frozen, is a regular part of breakfast. Oranges have become our leading fruit.

The native home of the orange is south China and Indochina. From there it spread to every part of the world having a suitable climate. The orange tree can stand only a few degrees of frost. Temperatures of 25° F. cause some injury, and below 20°, severe injury or death.

Oranges are of three principal kinds, each with many varieties. The most important in the United States and most other countries is the sweet orange, *Citrus sinensis*. The fruit is generally round to oval in shape, and the peel adheres rather tightly to the pulp, or flesh.

The mandarin, *C. reticulata*, has thin, loose skin that separates readily from the pulp. The pulp segments also separate easily. The mandarin includes the tangerines, having dark, orange-red peel, and the Satsumas, with lighter, yellow peel. Mandarin oranges are the kinds most extensively grown in China and Japan.

The third group, *C. aurantium*, has fruits too sour and bitter for eating out of hand. They are used for marmalade and some ade drinks.

Sweet and mandarin oranges undoubtedly have been eaten in south China since the country was inhabited. Oranges appear in Chinese writing as early as 2200 B.C., but their spread to other countries was relatively slow. The sweet orange is not mentioned in European writing until the 15th century.

As with the lemon, Columbus carried seed of the sweet orange when he sailed in 1493 to establish a settlement on Hispaniola. The orange flourished there, and early in the 16th century was taken to Mexico and Central America. It was planted in Florida when St. Augustine was settled in 1565, though it may have reached there even earlier.

Two centuries later settlers found many wild orange groves around the lakes in central Florida, particularly where Indian villages had been. One wild grove, described in 1764, was 40 miles long. But not until Florida became a part of the United States in 1821 did its commercial industry start.

Sweet oranges reached California with the founding of the mission at San Diego in 1769, and were carried to other missions as they were established. Some 400 trees planted at the Mission of San Gabriel about 1804 represented the first sizable citrus orchard in the State.

Mandarin oranges did not reach Europe until 1805. By 1850 they were well known in Mediterranean countries. The first introduction on record into the United States was by the Italian consul at New Orleans, who planted Chinese mandarins there between 1840 and 1850.

Researchers of the United States Department of Agriculture have crossed sweet oranges and tangerine oranges. Such crosses, known as tangors, have occurred naturally and are one of our most delicious citrus fruits.

The United States leads the world in orange production, with Florida growing the most, California a close second, followed by Texas, Arizona, Louisiana, and Mississippi.

Florida and California regulate the maturity, quality, and even the sweetness of oranges sold. To prevent diseases and molds which result from damaged skins, the fruit is picked by skilled workers who often wear soft cloth gloves. Conveyor belts carry the ripe oranges through successive washings in soap and water, borax solution, and clean water, where mechanical brushes scrub them. They are then dried in wind tunnels. Some are coated with wax for additional protection. Grading and packing into wood or fiberboard boxes are done by hand.

Spain, Brazil, China, Japan, Italy, and Palestine also produce many oranges; in fact, all tropical and subtropical countries do.

Oranges, Grown in Burma 4,000 Years Ago, Are the World's Leading Fresh Fruit. Sweet oranges and mandarins (tangerines) had spread west to Europe by the 15th century. Columbus took orange seeds to Haiti; Spanish settlers brought them to Florida and California. The United States now produces half the world supply.

The Ade Fruits, Lemon and Lime

LEMONS AND LIMES probably have more uses than any other citrus fruit. They are used to flavor fish, meat, pies, puddings, and other food. In the United States lemon juice is a popular ingredient in salad dressing and tea. Both fruits form the basis of ade drinks.

Their richness in vitamin C makes them valuable additions to the diet. Sales of lemons in this country are noticeably linked to the prevalence of colds as well as to hot weather. British sailors were nicknamed "limeys" because of the limes furnished them on shipboard to prevent scurvy, a disease caused by lack of vitamin C.

Yet, despite their value and versatility, both fruits are limited to a comparatively small share of the citrus market. The reason is obvious: in a beverage glass one small lemon or lime does the work of two or three good-sized oranges.

The lemon, *Citrus limon*, and the lime, *C. aurantifolia*, are linked botanically and historically. Both occur as sweet fruits, as well as the highly acid fruits we know. The sweet varieties are chiefly prized in Oriental countries.

Their native home is believed to be the warm, humid district east of the Himalayas, in northern Burma, and possibly in eastern India. Both fruits, however, have tended to naturalize in any country where they are well adapted, so the exact original home cannot be determined.

The Arabs established the lemon, and apparently the lime, in Persia and Palestine, where both undoubtedly were growing at the time of the Crusades. European writers mention lemons and limes only after that time, and there is strong evidence that Crusaders brought these fruits, as well as sour oranges, back to Europe. By the mid-13th century they were well known in Italy.

The date of the introduction of citrus fruits into the Western Hemisphere is well established. On his second voyage to the New World, to establish a colony, Columbus took seeds of many plants. He stopped at the island of Gomera, one of the Canary group, in October of 1493, and there secured seeds of oranges, lemons, and many vegetables. On the northern coast of the island of Hispaniola he established his colony, Isabela. Thirty years later citrus trees on the island were described as beyond counting.

The Spanish conquerors carried citrus fruits to the mainland of Mexico and Central America in the early years of the 16th century. The Portuguese had established them in Brazil by 1540. They were planted at St. Augustine, Florida, when the Spanish settled there in 1565. Soon groves of seedling citrus were spread by the Spanish and Indians to other parts of Florida.

Two centuries later Franciscan padres from Mexico established at San Diego the first mission in California. Presumably they brought with them fruits they had been cultivating, among them lemons and limes. California's commercial production began its great expansion after 1880.

Of today's two great centers of lemon production, one is southern Italy and Sicily. The other is southern California, mainly in the coastal counties, where the Pacific tempers winter cold and summer heat.

For years California lemons were considered inferior to the Italian because growers did not "cure" them before shipping, a practice commonly followed in Italy. Curing consists of picking the fruit green and allowing it to ripen in cool storage before packing for shipment. After adopting this practice, California's lemon industry grew rapidly. The State now supplies more than half the world's lemons.

The lemon is subject to serious diseases in hot, humid climates. An early lemon-growing industry in Florida was wiped out by a great freeze in 1894-95. It was never re-established, partly because of the disease problem which had harassed growers.

The lime thrives better than the lemon in hot, humid climates, being more resistant to fungus diseases. Egypt leads the world in lime production, both sweet and sour. Limes also are grown extensively in Mexico and the West Indian islands. United States production is mainly in south Florida, though California grows some.

Columbus Planted the First Lemons and Limes in the New World in 1493. Both types of citrus probably originated in Burma and spread west. Crusaders brought them to Europe from Palestine in the 12th century. More than half the world's lemons grow in the United States.

The Aristocrat of the Breakfast Table

AMERICA HAS GIVEN GRAPEFRUIT to the world, although the grapefruit, like most of us living in America, traces its ancestry to other lands.

In tracking down the grapefruit, we consider first the pomelo, or shaddock, *Citrus grandis*. The general abundance of trees indicates it probably originated in the Malay Archipelago and neighboring islands as far east as the Fijis.

The pomelo tree is large for citrus, and a vigorous grower. The fruit is also large, up to eight inches in diameter. It has the color and general appearance of a large, coarse, thick-skinned grapefruit, and the membranes that enclose the segments are extremely tough.

The pomelo apparently reached Europe about the same time as the lemon (by the mid-12th century). Known as "Adam's apple," it was grown mostly as a garden curiosity.

There is no record that the Spanish took the pomelo to the New World. It was first recorded in the West Indies in 1693 by Hans Sloane, in a catalogue of Jamaica plants. Its introduction to the Americas is credited to Captain Shaddock, the commander of an East Indian ship, who left seed of the pomelo at Barbados on his way to England. Captain Shaddock also gave the fruit its generally known English name.

Grapefruit presumably originated in the West Indies, but the exact place or manner of origin is unknown. It was first described under the name "Forbidden fruit" in 1750 by Griffith Hughes, in *The Natural History of Barbados*. Later the forbidden fruit, or "smaller shaddock," was said to be "cultivated in most parts of the country [Barbados]."

The name grapefruit originated in Jamaica, apparently either because the fruit was thought to resemble the grape in flavor, or because it is frequently borne in clusters. Characteristics of the grapefruit suggest a cross of the shaddock and the sweet orange. But its behavior in breed-ing or when grown from seed indicates it is not a hybrid. Its seed progeny is typically grapefruit, instead of showing characteristics of two parents. Most probably the grapefruit originated as a mutation of the shaddock.

Grapefruit from Barbados was described in 1750, but nearly 100 years passed before it was introduced into Florida by Odet Philippe, once a surgeon in Napoleon's navy. He planted trees at Safety Harbor, presumably from West Indies seed, about 1840. From these trees and their seed progeny most of our varieties have come.

For several decades thereafter the grapefruit was hardly known outside the State. No shipments were made to northern markets until after 1880. At the turn of the century grapefruit was still something to be stared at in fruit shops and talked about when served at the table. The grapefruit's subsequent rise in popularity has been meteoric.

Today's cultivated grapefruit trees grow from 15 to 25 feet high and have dark green leaves. A mature tree may produce up to 1,500 pounds of fruit a year. Earlier grapefruits were seedy, but a nearly seedless fruit was discovered near Lakeland, Florida, and propagated about 1890. This tree was the start of the nearly seedless variety, Marsh, now the most widely grown. Still later, mutations having pink flesh were found, some of them seedless, or nearly so. Today the pink-fleshed, seedless varieties command a premium at fresh-fruit markets.

Florida, cradle of grapefruit culture, still leads in this crop. Since 1925 there has been a great development in grapefruit growing in the Rio Grande Valley at the extreme southern tip of Texas. Arizona and California also produce substantial quantities.

When the fruit became so popular here, other citrus-producing areas took interest and today grapefruit are grown to some extent in all citrus-growing countries. But nowhere else has it become as popular as in the United States.

Grapefruit have been crossed with other kinds of citrus. Crosses with tangerines have produced fruits called tangelos. These are usually juicy, rather thin-skinned fruits which peel easily and have a rich flavor.

Grapefruit Evolved from the Shaddock, a Thick-skinned East Indian Fruit. First grapefruit, tart and seedy, were found in Barbados about 1750. Brought to Florida in the 1840's, grapefruit have since developed into our nearly seedless, semisweet breakfast and dessert fruit.

Banana, Fruit of the Wise Men

BANANAS are the most important tropical fruit around the world. Not only are they a major part of the diet for millions who live in the Tropics, but they are also a leading export. More than 100,000,000 bunches a year go into world trade, each bunch containing 10 to 20 "hands" of fruit and weighing about 50 pounds.

One reason for the banana's popularity is its high nutritive value. It is as much as 22 percent carbohydrate, a rich source of food energy; it also has vitamins A and C. These hidden benefits, moreover, are contained in a meat which is soft, sweet, and pleasantly aromatic.

Also in the banana's favor are the ease and speed with which it grows. Banana "trees" are really huge herbaceous plants which quickly shoot up to a height of 15 to 20 feet. The plant's true stem is underground and has buds, or "eyes," like a potato. These stems, or rhizomes, are transplanted to establish new plants; as with potatoes, each may be cut into several pieces.

The leaf-bearing stalks appear above ground three to four weeks after planting. The bloom appears ten or twelve months after planting, and the fruit matures five or six months later.

The botanical name of the common banana, *Musa sapientum*, means "fruit of the Wise Men." According to legend, the sages of India rested in the shade of the plant and ate of the fruit.

A second species, *M. nana*, the dwarf banana, is similar to the common banana. These two species, native to southern Asia, probably to India and the Malay Archipelago, contributed the varieties growing throughout the world.

The closely related plantains, or cooking bananas, *M. paradisiaca* and *M. fehi*, are important food in the Tropics. These fruits are not palatable raw since they remain starchy when ripe, but are excellent cooked.

The banana is one of the oldest known fruits, perhaps one of the first cultivated. Distinctive names in Sanskrit, ancient Chinese, and the Malay languages indicate it was known throughout much of prehistoric southern Asia.

Bananas were found on all the tropical Pacific islands when white men first visited them. Apparently the fruit traveled there with migrants from the Asiatic mainland. The first such migra-tion is believed to have occurred about the time of Christ. The banana was much longer in reaching the Mediterranean. The Arab poet Masudi, who died A.D. 956, extolled a dish popular in Damascus, Constantinople, and Cairo, a confection of almonds, honey, and bananas in nut oil.

Friar Tomás de Berlanga introduced the banana into the New World, bringing plants from the Canary Islands to Hispaniola in 1516. Shortly afterward bananas were taken to Mexico. The fruit thrived so well in the American Tropics that later visitors mistakenly thought the banana native to this continent.

Vessels occasionally brought a few bunches of West Indian bananas to American ports in the early 19th century. After the Civil War imports increased, but many shipments arrived overripe. Between 1870 and 1880 American planters established commercial production in Central America and, with steamships, delivery became more dependable. During the same decade Jamaica began regular shipments to Boston.

Growing and marketing conditions were chaotic; supply and state of the delivered fruit varied greatly. In 1899 the principal companies incorporated as the United Fruit Company.

Today the banana industry is one of the most highly organized fruit industries. Plantations are distributed throughout Central American countries, Colombia, and the West Indies, so that risk of crop failure through disease is minimized. Railroads have been built to carry the fruit from plantations to shipside. Refrigerated steamers transport it to United States ports; there the fruit is loaded into refrigerator cars for shipment to all parts of the Nation.

Large quantities are also marketed in Europe. The fruit of the Wise Men, food staple of the Tropics, is now a world-wide item of commerce.

Bananas Are the Leading Fruit of the Tropics. Greeks under Alexander the Great saw the fruit in its native home, India. Most bananas are now grown in the Caribbean area; half the world's exports go to the United States. Flower spike (inset) emerging at top of false trunk bends down to bear the bunch of fruit. Once the plants fruit they die. Planting to eating takes but 18 months.

Mango, an Evergreen from India

POSSIBLY MORE THAN any other fruit, mangoes have their critics and their enthusiasts. A true mango lover may develop an almost crusading spirit in promoting the fruit. In India, where mangoes are most widely grown and eaten, wealthy gardeners often collect mango trees; one such garden is reported to contain 500 varieties.

A leading American mango enthusiast was the naturalist, David Fairchild, who collected and cultivated many fine varieties at his Florida home (page 174). A chapter in his book, *The World Grows Round My Door*, extols "The Gorgeous East Indian Mango." This quotation from it reveals the feelings of a true mangophile:

"Every morning in mango time, as I walk along the path . . . I have to lower my head to avoid striking one of the beautiful Borsha mangoes swinging like a pendulum . . . I fondle it with my hands and watch the red blush growing larger and brighter every sunny day while its greenish-yellow tip turns to gold, my mouth watering for a taste of it."

On the other hand, the mangophobes, after tasting a single mango, have pronounced the fruit inedible. They complain of a strong, rank flavor: "it tastes like turpentine."

Why the sharp difference of opinion? The basis for it lies in the fruit itself. A superior variety of mango, properly ripened, is all that its supporters say it is—one of the world's finest fruits. An inferior or an unripe one is fibrous, tough, acid, and does have a flavor resembling turpentine. Early shipments of such inferior fruit from Florida to northern markets helped start the mango off on the wrong foot.

The cultivated mango, *Mangifera indica*, like the citrus fruits, is native to southeast Asia, probably also to the near-by islands. It has been important in India since the start of agriculture there. A mango grove is said to have been presented to Buddha as a place of repose. Akbar, who ruled northern India in the 16th century, is said to have planted an orchard of 100,000 trees, at a time when large orchards were unheard of.

The mango traveled slowly. The Portuguese probably carried it to East Africa, where it is now common, and introduced it into America. They planted it at Bahia (Salvador), Brazil, about 1700.

It reached the West Indies some 50 years later, and Mexico early in the 19th century.

Henry Perrine, a pioneer Florida horticulturist, took mangoes from Mexico to his place south of Miami in 1833. These trees apparently were lost after Perrine's death. A second introduction, about 1861 or 1862, was successful. These were seedling trees, however, and bore inferior fruit.

Early attempts to introduce choice Indian mangoes were unsuccessful, but in 1889 the U. S. Department of Agriculture brought in six varieties. Most of these trees died, but at least one of the high-quality Mulgoba variety survived. When it began to bear, nine years later, the superior quality, as compared to seedlings, attracted wide interest. Since then, many choice Oriental varieties have been established.

The mango is a large tree with dense, glossy, green foliage. It is most fruitful in areas having alternate wet and dry periods. Choice varieties are sensitive to cold—temperatures two or three degrees below freezing kill or injure the trees—and the roots will not tolerate waterlogged soil.

Though it is an important fruit in most tropical countries, the mango is still little known in this country. Its culture and market production here is limited to the southern third of Florida. Even under the most favorable conditions, yield of choice varieties has often been low.

Imports of the fruit are even more sharply restricted. Mangoes harbor the Mediterranean, the Oriental, and other fruit flies which might menace United States crops. For this reason, fresh mangoes are imported only from Mexico, and these only after special treatments.

Mexico and other large producing countries do some commercial canning. Comparable in quality to canned peaches, canned mango is rarely seen in our markets, though Indian chutney, made with mangoes, has had some sale here.

Mangoes, a Basic Fruit in the Tropics, Are Still Rare in America. Mangoes are native to southeast Asia. Portuguese planted them in Brazil about 1700; first successful Florida plantings came after 1860. The fruit, hanging like pendulums from long stems, may grow to four or five pounds. The finest varieties have a rich, spicy flavor.

Avocado and Papaya, Gifts of the Aztecs

TWO NATIVE AMERICAN FRUITS, the avocado and the papaya, are important in tropical areas around the world. The papaya is little known in the United States. The avocado, on the other hand, is shipped from California and Florida to markets all over the country.

Here the avocados are used mainly in salads or desserts. In parts of Mexico and Central America, however, they are often used as a meat substitute; the avocado is rich in protein and contains up to 30 percent of its weight in oil.

The avocado is native to Mexico and Central America. Before the discovery of the New World, avocados were growing possibly as far south as Peru, but were probably not present in the West Indian islands. The avocado was being used extensively by the Aztecs and other Indians when the Spaniards arrived. It is today an important part of the native diet where it grows. Tortillas, avocado, and coffee are considered an excellent meal by Mexicans and Central Americans.

Aztec picture writings had a sign for the avocado. The early Spanish spelling of the Aztec name was *ahuacatl*. The English name, avocado, is derived from Spanish modifications of the original Aztec word.

European visitors recognized the value of the rich, oily, nutritious fruit. Even so, it was slow to be transported to other tropical countries, perhaps because it does not propagate readily. The avocado was grown in the Hawaiian Islands as early as 1825, and has since been widely distributed in Africa and Polynesia. There are now plantings in most parts of the world where the climate is suitable.

The first definite record of avocado trees in Florida was of those horticulturist Henry Perrine brought from Mexico in 1833 and planted south of Miami. California's first recorded planting was at Santa Barbara in 1871, also with Mexican trees. Botanists recognize two species, both now important in commerce. The Guatemalan avocados, *Persea americana*, are relatively thick-skinned and the fruit ripens mainly in winter and spring. A subgroup, the West Indian race, ripens mainly in summer and fall.

The Mexican race, *P. drymifolia*, is much thinner skinned and withstands cold better than the Guatemalan and West Indian races. The races cross freely, and some of our most valuable avocado varieties appear to be hybrids. Enough varieties have been developed to make mature fruits available practically every month in the year.

The papaya, *Carica papaya*, or melon tree, is a unique contribution from the Americas. This very large, melonlike fruit spread quickly to other tropical countries after Columbus reached these shores. Before 1600, it had reached the Philippines, India, and probably Africa. Its showy, high-quality fruit and its ease of transport and propagation by seed account for its rapid spread. In fact, it spread so rapidly that for a time there was question as to whether its original home was America or Africa or India.

Whether it is native to the West Indian islands or the Mexican mainland, or both, remains a question. But not its American origin.

The papaya is a giant herbaceous plant, rather than a tree. The fruits range from one to 20 pounds and mature in about 18 months from the time the seed is planted. In frost-free countries plants produce for several years.

The papaya produces an enzyme, papain, that resembles pepsin in its usefulness in treating certain digestive ailments. Its major use is as a tenderizer of meats. India is the principal commercial source of papain.

Outside America, the papaya is of major importance in tropical Asia, Africa, and Hawaii. It is grown only in limited quantities in the United States, almost entirely in southern Florida. The heavy, very tender fruit is difficult to ship.

Neither papayas nor avocados tolerate temperatures more than a degree or two below freezing. Most of our avocados are therefore grown near the California coast, south of Los Angeles, and in south Florida. Avocados ship easily, however, and many Americans who never saw an avocado tree appreciate this gift from the Aztecs.

Papayas and Avocados from Tropical America Have Spread Round the World. Spanish Conquistadores found Aztecs and Incas growing melonlike papayas (left) and oily avocados. Papayas thrive in Africa, India, and Hawaii. Mexicans substitute protein-rich avocados for meat.

Columbus Found Pineapples in America

FEW AMERICANS KNOW what a really good fresh pineapple tastes like. Only those who have traveled or lived in the Tropics where they are grown know the soft, sweet, juicy fruit as it comes fully ripened from the plant. We can get just an inkling of the flavor by comparing sweet canned pineapple juice, made from ripe fruit without adding sugar, with the hard, tart fresh pineapples sold in grocery stores.

Why this great difference? A large quantity of starch is stored in the plant stem. Just before ripening, this starch turns to sugar and is carried into the fruit; the sugar content sometimes increases 100 percent in this last stage. Unfortunately, fresh pineapples cannot be shipped very far after they are fully ripe. For this reason, and because raw pineapple is troublesome to prepare, Americans eat most of theirs out of cans.

Columbus found the pineapple, *Ananas comosus*, on the island of Guadeloupe during his second voyage in 1493. The pineapple apparently had been brought to the West Indies by the Indians. Its native home is South America, in Brazil and probably Paraguay.

Its European name, *anana*, derives from the Guarani Indian language, in which *a* signified fruit in general and *nana* meant excelling. This tribe, native to Paraguay, overran the countries north to Panama and is believed to have spread the "excellent fruit" throughout northern South America long before Spanish explorers found the fruit in the West Indies and in Mexico.

The Spaniards called the fruit *"piña de Indias"* because of the general resemblance to the pine cone. The English called it pineapple, although it bears no resemblance to the apple. Other European tongues retained the native name, or slight modifications of it.

After the discovery of America, the fruit was quickly disseminated throughout the world. The fruit generally is seedless, but the suckers from which the plants are propagated will stand long handling and still grow. Thus there was no problem distributing the plants, even by slow sailing ships of the 16th century.

Fruits taken to Europe were greatly esteemed, and soon gardeners of northern Europe were attempting to produce them under glass. A wealthy merchant near Leiden, in the Netherlands, is credited with first producing mature fruit under glass, early in the 18th century. Glasshouse growers in England and on the Continent soon were producing fruit for sale, and numerous publications described growing methods.

This industry flourished during the 19th century, and growing pineapples under glass for the European trade is still a major industry in the Azores today. But development of large plantations in the Tropics, together with improved shipping facilities, has made commercial production under glass generally uneconomic.

Pineapples grow on a herbaceous plant with stiff, large, grasslike leaves. Because the leaves contain tissues especially adapted for retaining moisture, pineapples can survive long dry periods and grow in semiarid regions.

New plants are produced by setting the offsets, or shoots, taken from the mother plant. Where cultivation is on a large scale, as in Hawaii, the ground is often covered with asphalt-treated paper to conserve moisture. The shoots are set through holes in the paper. Rain or dew collects on the leaves and flows inward to the stem and down through the holes.

Between 15,000 and 20,000 plants are set to an acre. In 12 to 18 months after setting, each plant produces a single fruit on a stem two to three feet high. After the fruit is harvested, the shoots along the stem grow a second crop about 12 months later. A plant may last for years but fruit size tends to decrease. Commercial producers harvest two to five crops before the plantings are torn out and reset.

Although the pineapple is one of the most widely grown of tropical fruits, about four-fifths of the pineapples entering world trade come from the Hawaiian Islands; and most of these are sold in the United States.

Pineapples, Sweet and Spiny, Are America's Most Important Fruit Gift to the World. Spread from South America by early traders, pineapples rank next to bananas among tropical fruits. Center of cultivation is Hawaii, where the harvest of vast fields of low, leafy plants goes mainly into canned fruit and juice.

Even a Sour Persimmon Can Be Sweetened

IN THE SOUTH, children sometimes dare one another to bite into a green persimmon. Anyone foolish enough to accept the challenge undergoes a form of torture one sufferer described this way: "Your mouth feels as if it's trying to turn itself inside out."

Two species are common in the United States, one native, one imported from the Orient. Most varieties contain measurable quantities of an acid called tannin which, when the fruit is green, produces the famous mouth-twisting effect.

The tannin which causes the astringency can be rendered tasteless by sealing the fruit in tight containers for several days. In the Orient, the fruit is often placed in tubs from which *sake* (rice beer) has been removed, and the tubs are tightly covered. The presence of alcohol, long believed helpful in removing the astringency, apparently is not necessary.

The Oriental persimmon, *Diospyros kaki*, is one of the popular fruits of subtropical Oriental countries. Hundreds of varieties are known in the southern islands of Japan and in the south-central part of eastern China. The species evidently originated in southern China, possibly from an amalgamation of native species. That area has been so little explored by western botanists that the origin of the cultivated form is uncertain.

The *kaki*, as it is known in Japan, is a truly subtropical fruit not well adapted to the Tropics, nor able to endure winter temperatures below 10° F. Trees grow up to 40 feet high and, like native American persimmons, are usually dioecious; that is, a single tree bears only female, or pistillate, flowers or only male, or staminate, flowers. Both kinds must be present for satisfactory fruit production.

The Oriental persimmon reached France early in the past century, but seems not to have arrived in the United States until after Admiral Perry visited Japan in 1853. Grafted trees of the better varieties were introduced about 1870, largely through the efforts of plant explorers of the U. S. Department of Agriculture.

Early in the 20th century there was wide interest in these fruits throughout the southern States, particularly Louisiana and Florida, and in California. In many cases production was poor because of failure to provide pollinating trees. Also, in spite of its good qualities, the unknown fruit did not find a ready demand on American markets. The abundance of fruits on our markets makes the introduction of a new kind difficult. Today persimmons enjoy a moderate but steady sale. In large areas of the South they are valuable for home gardens and local markets. The trees bloom very late, rarely being touched by spring frosts.

The American persimmon, *D. virginiana*, is a fairly abundant tree from central Kansas and Nebraska eastward to Maryland, Virginia, and the Carolinas. A few trees are found as far north as southern New England and Michigan. This native persimmon impressed early explorers and settlers as a promising and valuable fruit.

"Plumbs there are of 3 sorts," wrote Capt. John Smith soon after settling at Jamestown. "The red and white are like our hedge plumbs: but the other which they call Putchamis grow as high as a palmeta. The fruit is like a medlar; it is first green, then yellow and red when it is ripe: if it is not ripe it will drive a mans mouth awrie with much torment; but when it is ripe, it is as delicious as an apricock."

Only sporadic attempts have been made to improve the native persimmon. A good many 19th century gardeners collected persimmon trees; the poet William Cullen Bryant was a persimmon enthusiast. But improvement has not gone beyond selecting wild trees bearing superior fruit. The work done in breeding blueberries indicates what could be accomplished by similar work with the persimmon. If the native variety could be successfully crossed with the Oriental, the possibilities of improvement would be great.

Meanwhile, persimmon lovers will continue to shake dead-ripe fruit from native trees in late fall, and eat it out of hand or use it in persimmon pudding, cake, or other culinary delights.

Persimmons Are Good When Ripe—but Don't Bite into a Green One! Small native American persimmon (top) grows wild in the South. The larger *kaki*, from China and Japan, is cultivated in California and southern States. Unripe fruit is strong in tannic acid. Capt. John Smith found the ripe ones "delicious as an apricock."

A Pan-American Union Produced Our Strawberries

THE STRAWBERRY is America's favorite cultivated berry. We enjoy the berries fresh or frozen for breakfast or dessert; cooked and canned, or made into unexcelled preserves, or as part of two of our most popular confections, strawberry shortcake and strawberry ice cream.

Strawberries grow from Florida to Canada and Alaska and in soils ranging from sand to clay. Because they are easy to grow, they are found in many home gardens. They are also one of the few crops part-time farmers can easily turn into profit. Spraying generally is unnecessary; moderate cultivating, weeding, fertilizing, and occasional transplanting are all the care they need, except that in colder parts of the country beds must be covered in winter, usually with one to six inches of straw.

Although strawberry species are native to most of the temperate regions of the world, the large-fruited, productive varieties come from the union of species found in the two Americas. As an important cultivated fruit, the strawberry is a recent addition to world horticulture.

Wild strawberries were found over much of Europe from the earliest days, being mentioned by Virgil (70–19 B.C.) and Pliny the Elder (A.D. 23–79). Not until centuries later, however, is there evidence of cultivation. Wild berries were planted in gardens at least by the 15th century. These European species bore good-quality fruit especially noted for aroma. But the fruits were small and the plants bore sparingly, and neither size nor yield improved under cultivation.

The colonists in eastern America were amazed at the abundance, plant vigor, and fruitfulness of the native strawberry, *Fragaria virginiana*. "Wee cannot sett downe a foote but tred on strawberries," wrote a Maryland colonist.

This strawberry was taken to France; the date given by Jean Rodin, gardener to Louis XIII, was 1624. From France it went to England and other European countries. The berries, even under cultivation, were small, although of good flavor and more productive than the old European kinds.

The next great event in the history of the strawberry was the introduction of South American plants from Chile. Long before the white men arrived, the Indians of Chile cultivated a better strawberry than the European or the wild North American varieties. Some plants bore fruit as large as walnuts. A Frenchman, Captain Frezier, took plants to France in 1712. A few years later the Chilean berries, *F. chiloensis*, were taken to England.

European gardeners must have planted the Chilean and the North American kinds in the same gardens, for there were chance crosses of the two; some were large-fruited, vigorous, productive plants, the ancestors of our modern varieties.

Not until shortly before 1800, however, were these improved varieties listed by American nurserymen. One, a variety from Europe named Pine, with *F. chiloensis* in its ancestry, became a parent of many varieties produced in this country. By 1825, strawberries were well established in home gardens and commercial culture was developing near the larger cities.

In 1838, Charles M. Hovey, a horticulturist at Cambridge, Massachusetts, introduced a variety grown from seed produced by cross-pollination. This variety, named the Hovey, not only was a sensational improvement but, so far as is known, was the first fruit variety of any kind originated in the United States by breeding. Its stimulus to fruit breeding proved great.

Since the latter half of the 19th century many amateur breeders have crossed and selected strawberries. The general quality of the varieties has continually improved. Several State experimental stations and the U. S. Department of Agriculture have large-scale breeding projects. Most of the outstanding new varieties of the past 20 years have come from this State and Federal work.

Strawberries are grown to some extent in every State in the Union. The largest centers of commercial production are in Louisiana, Tennessee, Arkansas, Oregon, California, North Carolina, New Jersey, and the sections of Maryland and Delaware east of Chesapeake Bay.

Strawberries Are the First Fruit of Spring in Most Temperate Lands. Small, sweet strawberries grow wild around the world (upper left). Best of the larger varieties cultivated commercially come from a chance crossing of North American and Chilean berries in the early 1700's.

Fruits That Grow Among the Brambles

MANY A BARE-LEGGED HIKER, pausing by a bramble that tore at his skin, has stayed to pick its fruit. In most parts of the temperate world this fruit would be one of two closely related kinds, blackberries or raspberries.

Both belong to the rose family and have similar histories. Both are native to Asia, Europe, and North America. If raspberries go a little farther north (to the Arctic) and south (to the Equator), blackberries are generally more abundant in temperate regions.

Both are quick to spring up in neglected fields, and for many years were more apt to be mowed or plowed under than cultivated. Their very abundance kept them from commercial planting and scientific breeding until comparatively late in horticultural history.

Pliny, the first century Roman naturalist, was the earliest to mention raspberries. He spoke of them as having come from Mount Ida in Greece. Centuries later the great Swedish botanist Carolus Linnaeus gave the name *Rubus idaeus* to the common European red raspberry, because of this reference to Mount Ida.

Not until 1629 did an English writer more than mention the fruit. In that year a work on orcharding devoted a short chapter to raspberries. It described red and white kinds, and recommended them for "an afternoones dish to please the taste of the sicke as well as the sound."

During the 19th century many varieties of high quality were selected or developed, particularly in northern European countries. Raspberries there derive mainly from the native species, *R. idaeus*, and many varieties are richly flavored.

American colonists found two kinds of raspberries growing abundantly: the red raspberry, *R. strigosus*, quite similar to the European; and a black fruited kind, *R. occidentalis*, now known as black raspberry or blackcap raspberry. Our cultivated varieties derive from these two, and from hybrids with European species. Named varieties appeared in America and Europe at about the same time. Several appeared in the *American Gardener's Calendar* (1806), one of America's first books on gardening and orcharding.

About the mid-19th century, great interest developed in fruit breeding. The most prominent raspberry breeder was Dr. William D. Brinckle, a Philadelphia physician. He introduced several excellent red raspberries. The Latham, probably the most widely grown variety, was originated by the Minnesota Experiment Station.

Though blackberries are divided into hundreds of species, two major kinds occur in Europe and America: upright growing forms and prostrate, or trailing, forms, often called dewberries.

Upright blackberries have stiff, erect canes and generally are very thorny. They propagate by suckers from the roots. Trailing blackberries have slender canes, are much less heavily thorned, and do not sucker. The tips of the canes, if in contact with the soil, strike root and establish new plants. Upright forms tend to have a stronger, more bitter flavor than the trailing forms.

American blackberries thrive in all except the coldest or driest areas. They are particularly abundant along the eastern seaboard, west to the Plains, and throughout the South, especially in Texas. Two high-quality species of dewberries also grow along the Pacific coast.

In Europe blackberry cultivation seems to have started in the past 50-odd years; in America it started sooner. In 1850 a bush-type variety, Dorchester, was named in Massachusetts; it was important for nearly half a century. About 1875 a dewberry, the Lucretia, was discovered in West Virginia and transplanted to Ohio. This is still the leading dewberry in more northern latitudes.

In recent years, three high-quality trailing types have been grown widely: the Youngberry, bred by B. M. Young of Morgan City, Louisiana; the Loganberry, apparently a cross between the Pacific trailing type and the raspberry, which originated in the garden of Judge J. H. Logan at Santa Cruz, California; and the Boysenberry, a variety quite similar to Youngberry, of chance origin in California. Unfortunately, all are tender in the colder parts of the country.

Thorny Blackberries and Raspberries Were Pests to Land-clearing Colonists. Raspberries grow wild from Arctic to Equator; blackberries chiefly in temperate areas. Since they are plentiful, efforts to improve them began late. Crosses produced Young- and Loganberries.

Indians Taught Us to Use Cranberries

WHEN THE PILGRIMS landed at Plymouth Rock, they found a thornless vine growing thick over most of the low, semiswampy areas. On the vines were red berries, unfamiliar and bitter to the palate. Later the Pilgrims learned that the Indians valued these berries highly, both as food (probably pounded with meat into a paste called pemmican) and as a poultice for blood poisoning.

The Indian name for them was *I-bimi*, "bitter berry." Perhaps because the berries were a favorite food of cranes, the colonists called them crane-berries, and eventually, cranberries. But whether they ate them at the first Thanksgiving dinner we do not know.

The record of that feast, contained in a letter believed to have been written by Governor Edward Winslow, tells that four hunters were sent out and killed enough fowl in one day to serve the company for a week. Chief Massasoit and a party of his tribe joined them for three days and added three bears to the larder. Cranberries would have blended admirably with this menu; the Indians were familiar with them and at that season they should have been plentiful. Beyond that the evidence does not go.

The American cranberry, *Vaccinium macrocarpum*, is native from Nova Scotia, Canada, to North Carolina and westward to Wisconsin. It is found mainly in low, swampy sites, particularly those that flood in winter and drain in summer. The coast of Massachusetts, particularly Cape Cod, was and still is a rich center of native cranberries.

For nearly 200 years settlers there harvested cranberries from wild vines. This wild crop was a considerable source of revenue to many farmers. Henry Hall, a veteran of the Revolution, is credited with being the first to cultivate the fruit. About 1816 he transplanted wild vines to a swampy site near Dennis. In 1832 the local paper printed a story of his work, stating that he produced about 70 bushels per acre.

Soon other Massachusetts growers were planting cranberries, and a little later culture started in New Jersey. Many plantings failed before growers learned the conditions necessary for success. Bog areas with peat soil are best; they should be leveled, the surface removed to eliminate weeds, and sand spread over the peat to promote the growth of vines. Bogs should also be laid out so that they can be drained quickly, either by large pumps or by natural flow, and can be flooded during winter, both to protect the vines from cold and to control insect pests.

Earliest plantings were of unselected wild plants, but growers soon began to choose highly productive plants with especially fine berries. These were propagated and became the basis of the present industry. Growers have produced as many as 300 bushels on a single acre.

Thus evolved one of our most intensive and complicated horticultural industries. Today it centers mainly in Massachusetts, Wisconsin, New Jersey, Washington, and Oregon. Massachusetts raises more than half the Nation's crop.

Cranberries are harvested chiefly with large rake-toothed scoops pulled through the vines to remove the berries. Special machines are used on some bogs. The berries must be sorted before they are sold. One early method was to roll the berries down a series of 10 to 30 steps. The good ones, being firm, bounced to the bottom like little rubber balls; the soft, damaged berries stayed on the steps. Grading machines today still depend on the ability of the good berries to bounce.

The American cranberry is not a cultivated crop outside the United States and Canada. In the far north of Europe a related but smaller-sized native fruit is harvested in great quantities. Neither the European nor the American species is cultivated extensively in Europe.

The tradition that helped give cranberries their start in America has held the industry back. Growers and canners produce far more berries and sauce than can be eaten at Thanksgiving. Their problem is to persuade housewives that cranberries are good to eat the year round, not just on one Thursday in November.

Pilgrims Found Cranberries Ripe and Ready for the First Thanksgiving Dinner. In 1677 Massachusetts sent King Charles II ten bushels of these berries as a gift, calling them "choicest product of the colony." Cranberries grow best in land that can be flooded in winter.

Blueberries Are Crops That Raise Themselves

WHEN FORESTS ARE CUT or burned away, blueberries are often among the first plants to spring up. Frequently they become the dominant vegetation, providing the landowner with a paying crop that requires little effort except picking.

If the field is completely neglected, taller shrubs and trees soon grow and shade or choke out the blueberries. Thus in New England and other areas where native blueberries are harvested it is a common sight to see a farmer burning or mowing his blueberry fields. The berries quickly spring up again; the second year after burning a maximum crop will be ready.

The blueberry group is probably the most widely distributed fruit in the world. Species are spread over Asia, Europe, and North and South America. They extend from the Tropics to the northern limits of human habitation, where they are a valuable addition to the Eskimo diet. Yet only in the United States and Canada is the blueberry a cultivated, horticultural crop. All blueberries grown in North America have been bred from species native here.

There is great confusion in the common names blueberry and huckleberry. In some areas the names are used interchangeably. The U. S. Department of Agriculture and most botanists and horticulturists now use the name huckleberry for the fruit of a related group of plants that have 10 rather large bony seeds. Blueberries, on the other hand, have a large number of very small, inconspicuous seeds—so small they are not noticed when eaten. Only blueberries are grown as a horticultural crop.

The blueberry thrives only on acid soils. Various species occur over most of the United States and Canada east of the dry prairies; also along the west coast, especially in mountain areas. Picking and selling wild blueberries is still an important industry in the coastal counties of Maine, the Appalachian plateau from New England to Georgia and Alabama, the Ozarks of Missouri and Arkansas, and the Cascade and Coast Range mountains of the Pacific States.

The fruit of at least seven species is harvested on a fairly large scale. Most important is the low-bush blueberry, *Vaccinium angustifolium*, dominant from New England west to Minnesota. Second is the high-bush *V. corymbosum*, found on the Atlantic coastal plain from New England to Georgia, and west to Lake Michigan.

Improvement of blueberries by breeding is the work of the past half-century. Two names stand out in the story of this research. One is Dr. Frederick V. Coville, late botanist of the U.S. Department of Agriculture, who was long Chairman of the Committee on Research of the National Geographic Society; the other is Miss Elizabeth C. White, a pioneer grower in Whitesbog, New Jersey. Miss White offered cash prizes for native high-bush plants producing the largest fruit, and thus was able to assemble many large-fruited forms.

Starting in 1909, Dr. Coville and Miss White made crosses among these superior plants. The result of many years of this work was the introduction of 18 varieties that have large fruit and attractive color, and ripen over a two-month period. The fruit of some is more than double the size of the largest wild berries. These varieties are the basis of today's extensive cultivated blueberry industry of New Jersey, Michigan, North Carolina, and other States.

In the far South, the rabbit-eye blueberry, *V. ashei*, is cultivated on a considerable scale. A number of varieties were selected from the wild, but only in the past decade has systematic breeding been undertaken. This species is well adapted to northwestern Florida and near-by States, areas within about 300 miles of the Gulf of Mexico.

Because of exacting soil requirements, blueberries are not widely adapted to upland garden culture. They can be grown on many acid soils, particularly if the soil is kept heavily mulched with sawdust, oak leaves, or similar material. In small gardens, birds often harvest the crop before it is fully ripe. Covering the plants is about the only way to save the fruit.

Blueberries, Most Widespread of Wild Fruit, Feed Tropical Tribes and Eskimos. Blueberries and their seedier cousins, huckleberries, grow wild in virtually all areas between the Poles. Botanists only recently started to improve blueberries, yet already have produced berries up to seven-eighths of an inch in diameter.

221

Two Berries Known Best for Their Jelly

CURRANTS AND GOOSEBERRIES, spicy-flavored berries used in America chiefly for cooking, are prime examples of how fruit can be improved and yields increased by cultivation and breeding. In its wild state, a gooseberry weighs less than a quarter of an ounce. Culture has increased the weight eight times over. An experimental farm in Ottawa, Canada, has achieved yields of more than 13 tons an acre.

Currants and gooseberries, related fruits of the genus *Ribes*, are native in the colder parts of Europe and North America. Although planted in many home fruit gardens in the northern United States they are not nearly so important here as in Europe. England, especially, grows great quantities for fresh fruit, jams, pies, and puddings.

The European histories of these two fruits are very similar. Neither grows well in southern Europe, except in the mountains, and neither is mentioned in early horticultural writings of the Mediterranean countries. Not until agriculture and horticulture developed in northern Europe did these fruits attain any importance.

Currants and gooseberries were first mentioned as garden fruit plants about the time of the discovery of America. Both fruits probably first attained importance in the Low Countries, particularly the Netherlands. At least one German writer described currants in some detail late in the 15th century. References in English writings begin about the mid-16th century.

The name currant is misleading. It apparently derives from the berry's resemblance to the currant or Corinth grape, a small seedless grape long grown for drying. So-called dried "currants" of commerce are actually dried grapes of this type, and not currants at all.

The origin of the name gooseberry is less certain. The obvious assumption is that it was once commonly served with goose. More likely the English name is derived from the Dutch name *kruisbes*, literally "cross-berry."

The currant was listed with other fruits and crop plants sent to the Massachusetts Bay Colony in 1629. Gooseberries also were sent to the New World then or shortly thereafter, though we have no record of the date. European currants did so well that little effort has been made to improve our native kinds, although many species of currants are native here. The commonly grown white and red varieties derive mainly from the European species *Ribes sativum* and *R. rubrum*. The best commercial varieties are probably hybrids of these two species.

Black currants of the species *R. nigrum* abound in northern Europe, and long have been credited with medicinal value. Recent research has shown them to be extremely rich in vitamin C. They are not grown to any extent here.

European gooseberries, *R. grossularia*, thrive in this country only in the cool Pacific coast regions where summers are dry. In the humid East, mildew disease attacks the European kinds so severely that culture is difficult.

Native American species resistant to the mildew, mainly *R. hirtellum*, began appearing in our fruit catalogues about a century ago. A little later, apparently natural crosses of European and American varieties were selected and today are the important kinds grown here. They combine European quality with the disease resistance and heat tolerance of native kinds.

Species of *Ribes* are agents in the spread of the blister-rust fungus so highly destructive to the valuable white, or five-needle pine. The fungus does not spread from pine to pine, but passes one stage of its development in the leaves of currants and gooseberries. For this reason, Federal and State Governments have spent millions of dollars to eradicate native *Ribes* and have prohibited by law their cultivation in areas where white pine is important.

Where growing is permitted, these fruits are valuable additions to home gardens in the North. Seldom used fresh, gooseberries are most often picked for cooking while still green. They are prized by those whose ancestry traces to northern Europe, where these tart, strongly flavored fruits are traditional favorites.

Currants and Gooseberries Grow in Northern Forests and on Mountainsides. Both currants (left) and gooseberries, prized for jam and pies, are native to America, Europe, and Asia. Cultivation is prohibited in many areas because the bushes harbor a fungus that kills white pines.

Index

Abel, Clarke 74
Abelia 74, ill. 75
Aconite 25
Adlumia fungosa 79
African-violet 68, ill. 69
Agriculture: beginnings of 18–19, 57, 73, 101, 102,
    171; development 25, 29, 101
Allegheny-vine 79
Allium, various species 155, ill. 154
Allspice 80
Almond, Flowering 79
Aloe, True 58, ill. 59
Althaea rosea 77, ill. 76
Amaryllis family 52, 57
Ananas comosus 210, ill. 211
Angels Trumpet 23, 82
Angiosperms 18
Antirrhinum majus 58, ill. 59
Apium graveolens 134, ill. 134
Apple 170, 171, 172, 176, ill. 173, 177
Apricot 182, ill. 183
Aquilegia coerulea 93
Arbutus, Trailing 97
Arnold Arboretum 13
Arrangement, flower 32, ill. 32–40
Artichoke 132, ill. 133
Arum family 64
Asparagus 131, ill. 130
Aster: China 77, ill. 76; New England 94
Avocado 209, ill. 208
Azalea 79, ill. 35; Flame 97, ill. 96; Japanese 79,
    ill. 78, plate VIII

Bailey, L. H. 88
Balsam, Garden 64
Banana 204, ill. 205
Banks, Sir Joseph 47, 80
Barberry ill. 34
Bartram, John 48
Bauhin, Caspar 140
Bauhin, Jean 20
Bean, W. J. 97
Bean: Common 99–100, 111, ill. 110; Lima 111,
    ill. 110; Snap 111, ill. 100, 110 *See also* Soybean
Beet 139, ill. 138

Belamcanda 77, ill. 76
Bellflower 51, ill. 50
Bellis perennis 51, ill. 50
Bergamot, Wild 94
Berlanga, Tomás de 204
Berries 171 *See also* Blackberry; Blueberry; Cranberry; Gooseberry; Raspberry; Strawberry
Beta vulgaris 139, ill. 138
Birdbath 46
Bird-of-paradise Flower 64, ill. 65
Bitterroot 93
Blackberry 217, ill. 216
Blackberry-lily 29, 77, ill. 76
Black-eye Pea 162
Blanket-flower 93, ill. 92
Blastophaga 197
Bleeding Heart 79, ill. 78
Blight *See* Diseases
Bluebell 51
Blueberry 221, ill. 220
Bo-tree 43
Borecole 122, ill. 123
Botany Bay, Australia 80
Bottle-brush 80, ill. 81
Bougainville, Louis de 13
Bougainvillea ill. plate VI
Bouncing Bet 29
Boxwood ill. plate X
Boysenberry 217
Brachycome iberidifolia 80, ill. 81
Brassica, various species 57, 122, 125, 126, 128, 140, 161, 166, ill. 123, 124, 127, 129, 141, 160–161, 167
Breadfruit 12, plate X, ill. plate IV
Brinckle, William D. 217
Broccoli: cauliflower or heading 128; sprouting 128, ill. 100, 129
Brussels sprouts 126, ill. 127
Bulbs 23, 57, 60, as storage mechanisms 52
Burbank, Luther 182
Butterfly-tulip 93

Cabbage 57, 125, ill. 124; Chinese 166, ill. 167; hard-heading 125, ill. 100, 124; loose-heading 125; nonheading 122, 125, ill. 123

Cactus 71, ill. 89
Cajuput tree 80
Caladium 64
Calendula officinalis 51, ill. 50
Calla 64, ill. 65
Calla palustris 64
Callistemon rigidus 80, ill. 81
Callistephus chinensis 77, ill. 76
Calochortus 93
Camellia 77, 79, ill. 76
Campanula, various species 51, ill. 50
Campion ill. plate XII
Candytuft 58, ill. 59
Canna 23, 85, ill. 84
Cantaloupe 150 151, ill.
Canterbury Bells 51
Caper family 85
Caprification 197
Capsicum 120, ill. 120–121; *C. frutescens* 120 ill.
Cardinal Climber 85
Cardinal-flower 67
Cardoon 132
Carica papaya 209, ill. 208
Carnation 20, 55
Carrot 99, 137, 152, ill. 153
Cartier, Jacques 125, 140
Cassava 18
Castor-oil-plant 67, ill. 66
Catesby, Mark 48
Cauliflower 128, ill. 129
Celeriac 135, ill. 134
Celery 134 ill.
Chapman, John 176
Chard, Swiss 139, ill. 138
Checkered-lily 52, ill. 53
Cheiranthus cheiri 55, ill. 54
Cherry 170, 171, 188, ill. 189; Flowering 79, ill. 78, plate VII
Chestnut 13
Chicory, witloof 131
Chive 155, ill. 154
Chlorophyll 18
Christmas-rose 25
Chrysanthemum 25, 27, 77, 79, ill. 37, 76
Cichorium, various species 131, ill. 130

Cicuta 137
Cinchona 14
Cinnamon 9, 12
Citron 145
Citrullus vulgaris 145, ill. 144
Citrus, various species 198, 200, 203, ill. 199, 201, 202
Clark, William 13, 93
Clarkia 93, ill. 92
Clary 94
Clayton, John 48
Claytonia 48
Clematis 77, ill. 76
Cleome spinosa 85, ill. 84
Clove Pink 55
Cloves 9, 12, 80
Clusius 47, 60
Cocozelle 118, ill. 119
Coffee 14
Coleworts 122, 125
Collards 122, ill. 123
Columbine 93, ill. plate XII
Columbus, Christopher 9, 10–11, 120, 159, 198, 200, 210, plate III
Compositae family 88, ill. 89
Cook, Capt. James 13, 80
Cook, O. F. 16
Corn: hybrid 16, 109, ill. 108; Indian *See* Maize; Maya corn god ill. 103; sweet 109, ill. 108
Cortisone, sources of 15
Cosmos 88, ill. 89
Coville, Frederick V. 221
Cowpea 156, 162, ill. 163
Cowslip 51, ill. 50
Crab apple 176
Cranberry 218, ill. 219
Cranesbill 68
Crescenzi, Pietro 44
Crocus 52, ill. 53
Cross breeding 16; fruit 173, 174, 182, 198, 215
Cross-pollination: flowers ill. plate XII; melons 119, 145; vegetables 117, 119, 126, 139, ill. 102, 104
Crowders 162
Crown Imperial 63, ill. 62
Crown-of-thorns 71, 88, ill. 70
Crucifer family 55, 165, ill. 54, 164
Cucumber 105, 158–159 ill.
Cucumis, various species 105, 150, 158, 159, ill. 150–151, 158–159
Cucurbita, various species 116, 117, 118, ill. 116–117, 118–119
Cup-flower 82, ill. 83
Curare 15
Currants 222, ill. 223
Cydonia oblonga 178, ill. 179
Cymling 118, ill. 119

Cynara scolymus 132, ill. 133
Cypress Vine 85, ill. 84

Daffodil ill. plate XI
Dahl, Andreas 87
Dahlia 23, 87, 88, ill. 86
Daisy 88; Michaelmas 94, ill. 95; Swan River 80, ill. 81; True or English 51, ill. 50
Darwin, Charles 13, 60
Date 192, ill. 193, plate IX
Daucus carota 80, 152, ill. 153
Delonix regia 71, ill. 70
Dewberry 217
Dicentra, various species 79, ill. 78
Didiscus coerulea 80
Diervilla 74
Digitalis, source of 55
Dimorphotheca, various species 67, ill. 66
Dioscorea 15, 114
Diospyros, various species 212, ill. 213
Diseases, plant 16, 60, 174, 175, 198, 200, 222; blight 106, 148; mildew 148, 151, 222
Doctrine of Signatures 19
Dorsett, P. H. 16
Drupe 182
Dye, saffron, source of 52

Eden, Garden of 31
Eggplant 160–161 ill.
Egyptian Lotus 73
Elecampane 25
Elephant's-ear 64
Elgin Gardens, N. Y. 49
Endive 131, ill. 130
Ericaceae family 97
Eriogonum 93
Erythronium montanum 93
Eschscholtzia californica 93, ill. 92
Eucalyptus 80, ill. 81
Euphorbia, various species 71, 88, ill. 70, 89
Evening-primrose family 82
Explorers, botanical 13, 14, 15, 22, 23, 30, 47–48, 67, 88, 93, 94, ill. 42, 46 *See also* under individual names

Fairchild, David 15, 16, 206, ill. 174
Festivals 25, ill. plates VII, XIV
Feverfew 25
Fig 43, 197, ill. 196
Fish-pelargonium 68
Flamboyant 71, ill. 70
Flowers: arrangement 32, ill. 32–40; origin, centers of 29, 30; uses: dye 52; food 23, 25, 26–28, 29, 51, 60, 73, 87; insecticides 25, 27; medicinal 25, 27; narcotics 23; perfumes 27, 90; soap 29 *See also* Cross-pollination; Festivals; Religion

Food plants: early cultivation of, 23, 73 *See also* Flowers; Pine nuts

Forsythe, William 90

Forsythia 77, 90, ill. 76

Fortune, Robert 13

Fountain, garden: origin of 45, ill. 29

Foxglove 25, 55, ill. 54

Fragaria, various species 215, ill. 214

Frangipani 90, ill. 91

Frankincense tree ill. 42

Franklin, Benjamin 15, 169

Frémont, Capt. John 13

Fritillaria, various species 52, 63, ill. 53, 62

Fruit flies 206

Fruits: distinguished from vegetables 105; early cultivation of 73, 171; enemies, insects and disease 174, 175, 206; improvement and selection 172, 173, 174, 175; industries 175, 198, ill. plate IX; origin, centers of 171, 172; propagation, methods of 171, 172, 173, ill. 173

Fuchs, Leonhard 82

Fuchsia 82, ill. 83

Fumitory family 79

Fungus: aids plants of Heath family 97; injurious 174, 200, 222

Gage, Sir William 185

Gaillardia pulchella 93, ill. 92

Galanthus nivalis 52, ill. 53

Garden, Alexander 48

Gardenia 48

Gardens: Assyrian 31; Aztec 47, 87; botanical 48, 49 *See also* Kew Gardens; Buddhist 43; Chinese 43, 45; Colonial, U.S. 45, ill. plate X; Dutch 45; Egyptian 31, 41; English 45, ill. 30, plate I; So. Africa 64; formal 41, 44, 45, ill. 29, plate X; French 45; "hanging gardens" 41; herb 94; informal 43, 44, 45, ill. plate XI; Mediterranean 57; miniature 43; Moslem 47, 63; patio 46, 47, 87; Persian 41, 43, 46, 63, ill. 62; Renaissance 45, ill. 28; rock 47; Roman 44, 45, 58; truck 105

Garlic 23, 155, ill. 154

Gautama, Siddhartha 43

Genetics 16

Geranium 68, ill. 69

Gerarde, John 114

Gerbera 67, ill. 66

Gesneria family 68

Gethsemane, Garden of, plate XV

Gherkin 158, 159

Gibberellin 17

Gilliflower 55, ill. 54

Gladiolus 68, ill. 38, 69

Goatsbeard 137

Golden Bells 77

Gooseberry 222, ill. 223

Grafting 172, 174, ill. 173

Grape 170, 173, 174, 191, ill. 170, 190; Corinth 222; Thompson seedless 172

Grape-hyacinth 57, ill. 56

Grapefruit 73, 171, 203, ill. 202

Grasses 17, 18, 109

Greengage 185

Groff, G. Weidman 20

Grosvenor, Gilbert 20

Guava 80

Gum Tree 80, ill. 81

Gumbo 73, 146, ill. 147

Hall, Henry 218

Hardenpont, Nicolas 178

Heartsease 27, 51, ill. 50

Heath family 97

Helianthus tuberosus 132

Helichrysum bracteatum 80, ill. 81

Heliotrope 19

Helleborus niger 25

Hemlock, Water 137

Henry, Prince ("The Navigator") 10

Herbs 25, 51, 94, ill. 31

Hibiscus, various species 68, 73, 79, 146, ill. 69, 72, 147

Hollyhock 29, 77, ill. 76

Honey Dew 150, ill. 151

Honeysuckle family 74, ill. 75

Horehound 94

Horticulture *See* Agriculture

Hosack, David 49

Hovey, Charles M. 215

Huckleberry 221

Hughes, Griffith 203

Humboldt, Alexander von 13

Hutchinson, John 67

Hyacinth 57, ill. 56

Hybridization: flowers 48, 49; fruit *See* Cross-breeding; vegetables 109, 118, 140 *See also* Cross-pollination

Hydroponics 17

Hyssop 94

Iberis, various species 58, ill. 59

Ikebana 32 ill.

Impatiens 64, ill. 65

Indian Shot 85

Insecticides, flower bases 25, 27

Insects, injurious 174–175, 191, 206

Inula 25

Ipomoea, various species 85, 114, ill. 84, 115

Iris, Florentine 27; Japanese 79, ill. 78; family 52, 77, 87, ill. 33, 40

Irrigation, 19, 63

Jack-in-the-pulpit 64

Japanese beetle 174–175
Jasmine 90
Jefferson, Thomas 49, 113, 118
Johnny Appleseed 176

Kale 122, ill. 123
Kalm, Peter 48
Kalmia 48
Kew Gardens 14, 20, 67, 169
Kniphofia, various species 67, ill. 66
Kohlrabi 126, ill. 100, 127

Lace-flower, Blue 80, ill. 81
Lactuca, various species 148, ill. 149
Laurel, Mountain 48, 97
Laurens, Henry 48
Lavender 94
Leek 155, ill. 154
Lemon 200, ill. 201
Lemon Balm 94
Le Notre, André 45
Lettuce 148, ill. 149
Leucojum vernum 52
Lewis, Meriwether 13, 93
Lewisia 93
Lilium, various species 48, 74, ill. 75
Lily: Avalanche 93; Humboldt's 74; Regal 13, 74,
    ill. 75; Tiger 74; family 52, 57, 63, 67, 155
Lime 200, ill. 201
Linnaeus, Carolus 20, 48, 57, 68, 87, 217
Livingstone, David 13, 99, 145
Lo han 20
Lobel, Matthias 20, 118
Lobelia 20, 67, ill. 66
Logan, J. H. 217
Loganberry 217
Lotus, East Indian 23, 29–30, 73, 79, ill. 72
Lotus-eaters 73
Louse, Root 174, 191
Luelling, Henderson 188
Lupine 19, 93, ill. 92
Lycopersicon esculentum 112 ill.

Maize 23, 25, 99, 101, 109, 111, ill. 103
Malus, various species 176, ill. 177
Mandarin orange 198, ill. 199
Mangifera indica 206
Mango 15, 206, ill. 207; blossoms ill. 174
Manioc 18
Manzanita 97
Marentonneau, Gaillard de 93
Marigold: African 90, ill. 91; Cape 67, ill. 66;
    French 90, ill. 91; Pot 51, 90, ill. 50
Mariposa 93
Marjoram 94
Martyr, Peter 11, 114, 120
Matthiola incana 55, ill. 54

Medicinal properties of plants 10, 14–15, 19, 20,
    25, 27, 51, 55, 58, 94, 131, 134, 137, 139, 143,
    146, 151, 152, 222 *See also* Scurvy
Melaleuca leucadendron 80
Melon Tree *See* Papaya
Melons *See* Muskmelon; Watermelon
Mendel, Gregor Johann 16, 156
Meyer, Frank N. 16
Michaux, André 30, 48
Migration, plant 13–14, 29, 30, 31, 101–102
Mint family 94
Mohammed 63
Momordica grosvenori 20
Monarda, various species 94, ill. 95
Monkshood 25
Mons, Jean Baptiste van 178
Morning Glory 85, ill. 84
Moss-pink 94
Mountain Fringe 79
Mount Vernon, Va. ill. plate x
Mourning Bride *See* Scabious
Musa, various species 204, ill. 205
Muscari, various species 57, ill. 56
Mushrooms 97
Muskmelon 105, 119, 150–151 ill.
Mustard: Chinese 166, ill. 167; Indian 161, 166,
    ill. 160–161; "Japanese" 161; family 55, 57
Mutations 16
Myrtle, True 80; family 80

Narcotics 23
Nasturtium 85, ill. 84
Nectarine 181, ill. 180
Nelumbium nelumbo 73, ill. 72
Nerium oleander 58, ill. 59
Nieremberg, John Eusebius 82
Nierembergia, various species 82, ill. 83
Nightshade family 112
Nurseries 49, 178
Nutmeg 12
Nymphaea 73

Okra 73, 146, ill. 147
Olea europaea See Olive
Oleander 58, ill. 59
Olive 58, 194, ill. 195, plate xv
Onion 23, 155, ill. 104, 154
Orange 171, 175, 198, 200, ill. 199
Origin, centers of *See* Agriculture; Flowers; Fruits;
    Vegetables
Ornithogalum 57, ill. 56
Orris-root 27
Oswego Tea 94, ill. 95
Oxlip 51
Oyster Plant 137

Paeonia, various species 74, ill. 75

Palm, Date 192, ill. 193, plate IX
Palm of Christ 67
Pansy 27, 51, ill. 50
Papain 209
Papaver, various species 63, ill. 62
Papaya 22, 209, ill. 208
Parsley 135, ill.
Paracelsus 19
Parsnip 137, ill. 136; wild 15
Pastinaca sativa 137, ill. 136
Patents, plant 16
Pea 156, ill. 157; English 156, 162; Southern *See* Cowpea
Peach 30–31, 170, 171, 172, 181, ill. 180; dwarfed 79
Pear 178, ill. 179
Pelargonium 68, ill. 69
Pennyroyal 94
Peony 74, 79, ill. 75
Pepper: Garden 120–121 ill.; True 120
Perfumes: flower base 27, 90
Perrine, Henry 206, 209
Persea, various species 209, ill. 208
Persimmon 212, ill. 213
Petroselinum sativum 135 ill.
Petunia 82, ill. 83
Phaseolus, various species 99, 111, ill. 110
Phlox, Summer Perennial 94, ill. 95
Phoenix dactylifera 192, ill. 193
Photoperiodism 17
Phylloxera 174, 191
Pimiento 121, ill. 120
Pincushionflower *See* Scabious
Pine: dwarfed 79, ill. 78; Italian Stone 58, ill. 59; White 222
Pine nuts 58
Pineapple 14, 171, 210, ill. 211
Pinus pinea 58, ill. 59
Piper nigrum 120
Pisum sativum 156, 162, ill. 157
Plant Industry Station, Beltsville, Md. ill. 102
Plantains 204
Plants: classification 20; discovery of 9–15; diversity of forms 99; evolution 18; importance to man 17, 18; improvement of 104–105, ill. 102, 104; industries 13–14, 16, 198; introduction of 15–16; names 19, 20, 99–100; number of species 20, 49; origin, centers of 99–101, 102, 146, 160; wild and cultivated 99, 104
Pliny 20, 128, 140, 151, 182, 185, 188, 215, 217
Plum 185, ill. 184; American 173, 187, ill. 186; Japanese 79, 182, ill. 183
Plumeria rubra 90, ill. 91
Poinciana, Royal 71, ill. 70
Poinsett, Joel R. 48
Poinsettia 48, 71, 88, ill. 89
Poison-gas-bush 71

Poisons: in plants 23, 25, 60, 111, 112, 137, 143
Poker-plant 67, ill. 66
Pollination 159, 192, 197 *See also* Cross-pollination
Polo, Marco 10, 74
Polyanthus 51, ill. 50
Pomelo 73, 203 *See also* Shaddock
Pool, garden 44, 45, 63
Poppy, California 93, ill. 92; Oriental 63, ill. 62
Potato 99, 106, ill. 107
Potted plants: origin of 47
Primrose 51
Prince Nursery, Long Island, N. Y. 178
Privet, California ill. 44
Propagation, plant *See* Fruits; Pollination
Prune 185
Prunus, various species 181, 182, 185, 187, 188, ill. 180, 183, 184, 186, 189
Pumpkin 116, 117, 119 ill.
Punk Tree 80
Pyrethrum 25, 27
Pyrus, various species 178, ill. 179

Quamoclit, various species 85, ill. 84
Quarantine 16
Queen-Anne's-lace 80
Quince 178, ill. 179
Quinine, source of 14

Raab 128
Radiation genetics 16
Radish 165, ill. 164
Raisin 191
Raphanus, various species 165, ill. 164
Raspberry 217, ill. 216
Rauwolfia 15
Ravenala madagascariensis 71, ill. 70
Ray, John 20
Recipes, flower 26, 27, 28
Red-hot-poker 67
Religion, plants in 9, 19, 25, 30, 32, 42, 46–47, 51, 94; garden, influenced by, Asia 63
Rheum rhaponticum 143, ill. 142
Rhododendron, various species 79, 97, ill. 78, 96, plate VIII
Rhubarb 143, ill. 142
Ribes, various species 222, ill. 223
Ricinus communis 67, ill. 66
Rock, Joseph 13
Romaine 148, ill. 149
Rose 30, 51, ill. 39, plates II, XII
Rose-of-China 73, ill. 72
Roselle 146
Rosemallow 73
Rosemary 94
Royal Agricultural College, Cirencester, England 128, 137

Royal Botanic Gardens, England 14, 20, 67, 169
Rubber 11, 14
Rubus, various species 217, ill. 216
Rue 27
Rug designs: origin 42–43, 63
Rutabaga 140, ill. 141

Saffron 52
Sage: Common 94; Scarlet 82, ill. 83
Saint Paul, Baron Walter von 68
Saintpaulia ionantha 68, ill. 69
Salsify 137, ill. 136
Salvia splendens 82, ill. 83
Saponaria 29
Savory 94
Scabious, Sweet 25, 55, ill. 54
Scolymus hispanicus 137
Scorzonera 137
Scurvy 11, 64, 200
Seasoning: plants for 32, 51, 52, 55, 80, 94, 121, 134, 135, 161 *See also* Spices
Shaddock 171, 203 *See also* Pomelo
Sheng-Nung 74
Sherwood Gardens, Baltimore, Md. ill. plate XVI
Skunk cabbage 64
Sloane, Hans 203
Sloe 187
Smallage 134
Smith, Capt. John 182, 197, 212
Smuts, Jan Christiaan 67
Snakes-head 52, ill. 53
Snapdragon 58, ill. 59
Snowdrop 52, ill. 53
Snowflake 52
Soapwort 29
Soja max See Soybean
Solander, Daniel 80
Solandra 80
Solanum, various species 106, 160, ill. 107, 160
Soybean 16, 169, ill. 168
Spices 9, 10, 11–12, 80, 94, 120–121 ill.
Spider Flower 85, ill. 84
Spinach 156, ill. 157
Squash: summer 116, 118–119 ill.; winter 116–117 ill.
Star-of-Bethlehem 57, ill. 56
Stock 55, ill. 37, 54
Storksbill 68
Strangler-tree 71
Strawberry 215, ill. 214
Strawflower 80, ill. 81
Strelitzia reginae 64, ill. 65
Strophanthus 15
Sullivan, Gen. John 137, 152
Sunflower family 67, 88, ill. 89
Sweet potato 23, 85, 100, 114, ill. 115
Swingle, Walter T. 16, 20, plate IX

Tagetes, various species 90, ill. 91
Tangerine 198, 203, ill. 199
Tangelo 203
Tangor 198
Tannin 212
Taro 64
Tea 12, 77, 79, ill. plate V
Teosinte 109
Terrace gardening 41
Theophrastus 20, 135, 139, 176, 188
Thyme 94
Tiger-flower 87, ill. 86
Tobacco 11, 17, 82
Tomato 16, 19, 82, 105, 112–113, ill. 102, 112–113
Topiary art 44, 45, ill. 25, 44, plate X
Torch-flower 67
Trachymene coerulea 80, ill. 81
Tragopogon porrifolius 137, ill. 136
Travelers-tree 71, ill. 70
Trees: dwarfed 43, 79, ill. 78 *See also* under individual names
Tripsacum 109
Tropaeolum majus 85, ill. 84
Truck crops 105, 145, 150
Tulip 16, 60, ill. 61
Turnip 140, ill. 141

U. S. Department of Agriculture 173–174, 192, 198, 206, 215, 221, ill. 102, plate XIII; Section of Seed and Plant Introduction 15
Usambara 68

Vaccinium, various species 218, 221, ill. 219, 220
Van Dersal, William 97
Varro, Marcus Terentius 188
Vegetable marrows 118
Vegetables: definition 105; improvement of 104–105, ill. 102, 104; names, multiplicity of 99–100; origin, centers of 99–101, 102; wild forms 99, 104
Vegetative propagation 172
Verbena, Garden 82, ill. 83
Viburnum carlesi 74
Victoria, various species 85, ill. 84
Vigna, various species 162, ill. 163
Violet: *Viola tricolor* 51, ill. 50; African (Usambara) 68
Viruses, plant 60, 174, 175
Vitis, various species 191, ill. 190

Wallflower 55, ill. 54
Washington, George 15, 49, 162, plate X
Water-lily 42; Victoria 85, ill. 84 *See also* Lotus
Water supply 45, 47, 63, ill. 29, 62
Watermelon 13, 99, 119, 145, ill. 144
Weed 94
Weigela 17, 74

Well 47, 63
White, Elizabeth C. 221
Wickham, Henry 14
Wild Bergamot 94
Wild flower 94; difficult to domesticate 93
Willdenow, Karl Ludwig 88
Wilson, Ernest 13
Wistar, Caspar 79, 90
Wisteria 79, 90, ill. 78
Woundwort 94

X ray: burns, treatment of 58; mutations by 16

Yam 15, 114
Young, B. M. 217
Youngberry 217

Zantedeschi, Francesco 64
Zea mays 109 *See also* Maize
Zinnia 88, ill. 89
Zucchini 118, ill. 119

For *Additional* Reference

Many informative articles dealing with plants, gardens, agriculture, and other subjects discussed in this book can be found in the *National Geographic Magazine*. Refer to the NATIONAL GEOGRAPHIC MAGAZINE CUMULATIVE INDEX.

Comprehensive studies of civilizations and cultures which contributed many of our garden plants are found in two volumes of the National Geographic *Story of Man* Library:

INDIANS OF THE AMERICAS · *392 illustrations*
  262 paintings and photographs in full color · 432 pages $7.50

EVERYDAY LIFE IN ANCIENT TIMES · *215 illustrations*
  120 full-page paintings in color · 356 pages $6.00

Readers of the present volume will find stimulating, informative reading in other recently published books in The Society's *Natural Science* Library:

THE NATIONAL GEOGRAPHIC BOOK OF DOGS · *342 illustrations*
  189 paintings and photographs in full color · 432 pages $9.85

THE BOOK OF FISHES · *377 illustrations*
  207 paintings and photographs in full color · 340 pages $7.00

The above books are obtainable only from the National Geographic Society, Washington 6, D.C. Prices include postage. Publications brochure sent on request.

For further reading, the authors of THE WORLD IN YOUR GARDEN recommend:

THE STORY OF GARDENING; from the Hanging Gardens of Babylon to the Hanging Gardens of New York, by Richardson Wright

MEN AND GARDENS by Nan Fairbrother

HORTUS SECOND by L. H. and E. Z. Bailey

A DICTIONARY OF PLANT NAMES by H. L. Gerth van Wijk

MANUAL OF CULTIVATED TREES AND SHRUBS by A. Rehder

TROPICAL GARDENING AND PLANTING by H. F. Macmillan

ORIGIN OF CULTIVATED PLANTS by A. de Candolle

STURTEVANT'S NOTES ON EDIBLE PLANTS edited by U. P. Hedrick

BOTANICAL-GEOGRAPHIC PRINCIPLES OF SELECTION by N. I. Vavilov

THE ORIGIN OF INDIAN CORN AND ITS RELATIVES by P. C. Mangelsdorf and R. G. Reeves

MANUAL OF TROPICAL AND SUBTROPICAL FRUITS by Wilson Popenoe

TROPICAL FRUITS by O. H. Barrett

THE FIG by Ira J. Condit

PINEAPPLE by Maxwell O. Johnson

THE CITRUS INDUSTRY by H. J. Webber and L. D. Batchelor

NATIONAL GEOGRAPHIC
Society

National Geographic Magazine

16th & M Streets N.W.   Washington 6, D. C.

ORGANIZED IN 1888 "FOR THE INCREASE AND DIFFUSION OF GEOGRAPHIC KNOWLEDGE

North
America

Pacific
Ocean

Atlantic
Ocean

Central
America

South
America

I.E.Alleman